# THE ULTIMATE
# FC BAYERN MUNICH
# TRIVIA BOOK

A Collection of Amazing Trivia Quizzes
and Fun Facts for Die-Hard Bayern Fans!

Ray Walker

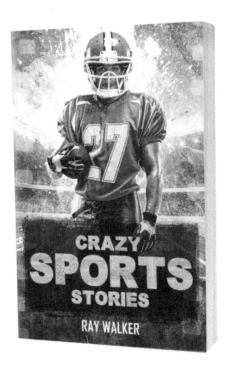

# CONTENTS

Introduction ..................................................................1

Chapter 1: Origins & History ..................................3

   Quiz Time! ...........................................................3

   Quiz Answers ......................................................8

   Did You Know? ...................................................9

Chapter 2: The Captain Class ..............................12

   Quiz Time! .........................................................12

   Quiz Answers ....................................................17

   Did You Know? .................................................18

Chapter 3: Amazing Managers .............................22

   Quiz Time! .........................................................22

   Quiz Answers ....................................................27

   Did You Know? .................................................28

Chapter 4: Goaltending Greats .............................32

   Quiz Time! .........................................................32

Quiz Answers...................................................37

Did You Know?.............................................38

## Chapter 5: Daring Defenders .................................42

Quiz Time!.......................................................42

Quiz Answers...................................................47

Did You Know?.............................................48

## Chapter 6: Maestros of the Midfield ...............52

Quiz Time!.......................................................52

Quiz Answers...................................................57

Did You Know?.............................................58

## Chapter 7: Sensational Strikers & Forwards .........63

Quiz Time!.......................................................63

Quiz Answers...................................................68

Did You Know?.............................................69

## Chapter 8: Notable Transfers & Signings ...........73

Quiz Time!.......................................................73

Quiz Answers...................................................78

Did You Know?.............................................79

## Chapter 9: Odds & Ends .................................84

Quiz Time!.......................................................84

Quiz Answers.................................................................89

Did You Know?.............................................................90

**Chapter 10: Domestic Competition** .............................**93**

Quiz Time!....................................................................93

Quiz Answers.................................................................98

Did You Know?.............................................................99

**Chapter 11: Europe & Beyond**......................................**103**

Quiz Time!..................................................................103

Quiz Answers...............................................................108

Did You Know?...........................................................109

**Chapter 12: Top Scorers** ..............................................**114**

Quiz Time!..................................................................114

Quiz Answers...............................................................119

Did You Know?...........................................................120

**Conclusion** .................................................................**125**

# INTRODUCTION

Just over 120 years ago, Bayern Munich was formed in Germany, and the team has been solidifying its hold on the title of the nation's most successful soccer club year after year. Two world wars couldn't slow them down, and it appears the Covid-19 pandemic hasn't hurt their momentum either.

Known as Die Roten ("The Reds") by many of their feverish fans, the Bundesliga club holds numerous records in its homeland, including the most league titles and German Cups. But Bayern Munich isn't just a hit in their homeland; the club has been one of the most successful ever in Europe, as well.

Bayern fans, nicknamed "Bavarians," have a lot to be proud of, and the team's worldwide following is growing with each passing year as fans across the globe are attracted to this incredibly entertaining team.

It may have taken 32 years for Bayern to win its first major league title, and although admittance to the Bundesliga wasn't automatic in 1963, the squad has never looked back once, making its debut in the nation's top flight two years later.

Second best simply isn't good enough for the club and its fans. Their striving for excellence and their never-say-die attitude are just two of the reasons they have earned such a tremendous amount of silverware throughout their colorful and storied history.

Bayern supporters have seen some of the world's top players suit up for Die Roten through the years, with superstars such as Franz Beckenbauer, Sepp Maier, Gerd Müller, Paul Breitner, Karl-Heinz Rummenigge, Lothar Matthäus, Oliver Kahn, Philipp Lahm, Arjen Robben, Robert Lewandowski, and Manuel Neuer gracing their pitch.

This trivia book was written to celebrate Bayern Munich's remarkable achievements by re-living its history from day one until January 1, 2021. You'll be able to meet the team's most beloved players and managers and find out how each has left his individual mark on the club.

The club's history is represented here in quiz form with 12 unique chapters, each covering a different topic. Each section features 20 stimulating quiz questions along with 10 riveting "Did You Know" facts. The questions are presented in multiple-choice and true-false options, and the answers are available on a separate page.

This is the perfect way to challenge yourself on the famous history of Bayern Munich and, of course, to challenge other Bavarians and soccer fans to quiz showdowns. The book will help refresh your knowledge of your favorite team and help you prepare for any challenges that come your way.

# CHAPTER 1:

# ORIGINS & HISTORY

## QUIZ TIME!

1. In what year was FC Bayern Munich founded?

    a. 1902
    b. 1901
    c. 1900
    d. 1899

2. Before the formation of the Bundesliga in 1963, German teams played in various sub-regional leagues, meaning Bayern played in approximately five different leagues between 1905 and 1914.

    a. True
    b. False

3. Which club did Bayern play its first match against in 1901?

    a. FC Hanau 93
    b. FC Heilbronn
    c. Karlsruher FV
    d. FC Nürnberg

4. In Bayern's first officially recorded season, how many games did the club win out of six?

    a. 6

    b. 5

    c. 4

    d. 3

5. Where was Bayern's first game played?

    a. Leopoldstraße

    b. Theresienwiese

    c. Schyrenplatz

    d. Grünwalder Stadion

6. How many times has Bayern Munich been relegated in the Bundesliga?

    a. 1

    b. 2

    c. 3

    d. The club has never been relegated.

7. In 1906, Bayern was struggling financially and did not have a place to play, so they merged with Münchner Sport-Club to stay afloat.

    a. True

    b. False

8. Who was the key founding member of Bayern Munich?

    a. Hans Kahn

    b. Franz John

    c. Fritz Weber

    d. Franz Braun

9. Bayern remained independent from Münchner Sport-Club after the two merged, but Bayern conceded which of the following?

   a. They had to play several Münchner Sport-Club players each game.
   b. They would rename themselves Münchner Sport-Club von Munich.
   c. They wore the kit colors of Münchner Sport-Club, red shorts and white shirts.
   d. They deferred 50% of all sponsorship payments to Münchner Sport-Club.

10. After the Second World War ended, which league did Bayern join?

   a. Oberliga Süd
   b. Regionalliga Süd
   c. Bundesliga Aufstiegsrunde
   d. Kreisliga Südbayern

11. Which of the following is NOT true about the hardships Bayern experienced during World War II?

   a. Kurt Landauer, the club's Jewish president, fled Germany.
   b. The Bayern offices were destroyed in a bombing raid.
   c. Bayern was banned from all league activities.
   d. Approximately 56 members of the club were casualties during the war.

12. When the Bundesliga was formed in 1963, Bayern was not one of the five teams from the Oberliga Süd that were accepted.

a. True

b. False

13. Bayern captain Konrad Heidkamp saved the club's trophies from destruction and theft during the Second World War by hiding them where?

    a. The basement of his house in Ismaning, Munich
    b. With his brother in Sweden
    c. A farm in Ascholding, Munich
    d. Buried on Rose Island in Lake Starnberg

14. Which regional rival was admitted to the Bundesliga instead of Bayern despite finishing below them in the final Oberliga Süd season?

    a. FC Augsburg
    b. VfB Stuttgart
    c. FC Nürnberg
    d. TSV 1860 Munich

15. How many goals did Bayern score in its first Oberliga Süd season in 1945-46?

    a. 67
    b. 75
    c. 61
    d. 53

16. When Bayern made their Bundesliga debut, they faced off against future rivals Borussia Dortmund.

    a. True
    b. False

17. Bayern's motto, "mia san mia," translates to what in English?

    a. Score and score again
    b. We are who we are
    c. We are the best
    d. We love the reds

18. Which year was Bayern's first season in the Bundesliga?

    a. 1963-64
    b. 1964-65
    c. 1965-66
    d. 1966-67

19. What color was Bayern's original crest?

    a. Blue
    b. Gold
    c. Red
    d. Green

20. As recently as 2017, Bayern shared Allianz Arena with TSV 1860 Munich.

    a. True
    b. False

# QUIZ ANSWERS

1. C – 1900

2. A – True

3. D – 1. FC Nürnberg

4. B – 5

5. B – Theresienwiese

6. D – The club has never been relegated.

7. A – True

8. B – Franz John

9. C – They wore the kit colors of Münchner Sport-Club, red shorts and white shirts.

10. A – Oberliga Süd

11. C – Bayern was banned from all league activities.

12. A – True

13. C – A farm in Ascholding, Munich

14. D – TSV 1860 Munich

15. A – 67

16. B – False

17. B – We are who we are

18. C – 1965-66

19. A – Blue

20. A – True

# DID YOU KNOW?

1. Generally referred to as Bayern Munich in English, the famous German Bundesliga club, located in Bavaria, is also known as Fußball-Club Bayern München, FC Bayern München, FCB, and FC Bayern. The club also has several nicknames such as Die Roten (The Reds), Der FCB (The FCB), Stern des Südens (Star of the South), Die Bayern (The Bavarians), and FC Hollywood. Bayern Munich is the most successful club in the history of German football, with a record 30 national league titles, as of 2020, along with 20 German national cups and numerous European trophies.

2. The club was founded by a group of players led by Franz John of Berlin in February 1900. The squad's main colors are red and white, while the team's crest features Bavaria's blue and white flag. As far as rivalries go, Bayern Munich generally doesn't see eye to eye with several teams including TSV 1860 Munich, 1. FC Nürnberg, Borussia Dortmund, and 1. FC Kaiserslautern. Matches with Dortmund are nicknamed "Der Klassiker," which means The Classic in English.

3. The Bayern Munich club was originally formed when members of the Munich Gymnastics Club were told they wouldn't be allowed to enter a squad in the German Football Association. The team then began playing and

beating numerous local rivals and made it to the semifinals of the South German championship in 1900-01.

4. Because of financial restrictions and the lack of an available pitch, Bayern joined forces with the Münchner Sport-Club (MSC) in January 1906, but remained an independent club. However, Bayern adopted the MSC colors and wore white shirts with red shorts. Bayern's original kit colors were supposed to be white and blue, but they wore white shirts and black shorts until joining MSC.

5. In 1907, Bayern started playing its home contests at a ground on Leopoldstraße and won the Eastern District Championship in 1910. The club went unbeaten in the next campaign to defend the title. The team currently plays its home games at the Allianz Arena, having moved there before the 2005-06 campaign. Before that, Bayern spent 33 years at the Olympiastadion.

6. After winning a few more local trophies, Bayern joined the newly formed Kreisliga in 1910-11. Bayern won the regional Bavarian league in its inaugural season and again in 1914, just before all soccer leagues were halted due to the outbreak of World War I.

7. After the war, Bayern won several regional events and, in 1926, captured its first South German championship. The club's first German national league title came six years later, in 1932, with a 2-0 win over Eintracht Frankfurt in the final.

8. After World War II, Bayern joined the Oberliga Süd, which was the Southern Conference of the country's First

Division. The team struggled, though, and went through 13 different managers from 1945 to 1963. Former club president, Kurt Landauer, returned to Germany in 1947 after being in exile during World War II and took control of the team again until 1951.

9.  Bayern was relegated in 1955 but managed to earn promotion back to the Oberliga the following season. The club also won the DFB-Pokal (German FA Cup) for the first time in 1956-57 by blanking Fortuna Düsseldorf 1-0 in the final.

10. In 1963, the five German Oberligas joined together to form one national league, which was named the Bundesliga. Five clubs from the Oberliga Süd were admitted to the Bundesliga based on their accumulated records for the previous 12 years. However, Bayern was ranked sixth and was eventually promoted to the Bundesliga in 1965.

# CHAPTER 2:

# THE CAPTAIN CLASS

## QUIZ TIME!

1. From the inception of the Bundesliga to 2020, how many players have been named full-time captains of Bayern Munich?

    a. 15
    b. 16
    c. 17
    d. 18

2. Werner Olk was named the club's first captain in the Bundesliga era.

    a. True
    b. False

3. Who was the first goalkeeper appointed full-time captain by Bayern?

    a. Dieter Hoeneß
    b. Manfred Müller
    c. Walter Junghans
    d. Sepp Maier

4. What year was Gerd Müller appointed captain for part of the season?

    a. 1976

    b. 1977

    c. 1978

    d. 1979

5. Which captain famously led the club to three consecutive European Cups?

    a. Paul Breitner

    b. Klaus Augenthaler

    c. Stefan Effenberg

    d. Franz Beckenbauer

6. Who captained the club from 2011 to 2017?

    a. Toni Kroos

    b. Philipp Lahm

    c. Arjen Robben

    d. Manuel Neuer

7. Franz Beckenbauer holds the title of honorary captain of both Bayern Munich and the German national team.

    a. True

    b. False

8. How many years was Oliver Kahn captain of the squad?

    a. 3

    b. 4

    c. 5

    d. 6

9. Who was Bayern's first captain in the 2000s?

   a. Carsten Jancker

   b. Oliver Kahn

   c. Thomas Helmer

   d. Stefan Effenberg

10. In 2017, Bayern appointed which of these players as skipper?

    a. Manuel Neuer

    b. Thomas Müller

    c. Robert Lewandowski

    d. Jérôme Boateng

11. Which defender captained Bayern in 1979-80?

    a. Bernd Gersdorff

    b. Klaus Augenthaler

    c. Georg Schwarzenbeck

    d. Bernhard Dürnberger

12. Between 2010 and 2020, Bayern had five different full-time captains.

    a. True

    b. False

13. Who wore the armband from 1991 to 1994?

    a. Oliver Kreuzer

    b. Raimond Aumann

    c. Thomas Berthold

    d. Manfred Bender

14. How many years was Paul Breitner captain of the club?

    a. 4

    b. 3

    c. 2

    d. 1

15. Who was Bayern's captain in 1983-84?

    a. Norbert Eder

    b. Roland Wohlfarth

    c. Holger Willmer

    d. Karl-Heinz Rummenigge

16. Franz Beckenbauer and Thomas Helmer share the record as the longest-serving captains of Bayern, holding the position for seven years each.

    a. True

    b. False

17. Who was the club's first non-German captain?

    a. Robert Lewandowski

    b. Arjen Robben

    c. Mark van Bommel

    d. Thiago

18. Who was named captain in 1994?

    a. Christian Ziege

    b. Markus Schupp

    c. Lothar Matthäus

    d. Thomas Helmer

19. Who was vice-captain during the 2018-19 season?

   a.  Thomas Müller
   b.  David Alaba
   c.  Franck Ribéry
   d.  Arjen Robben

20. As of 2020, Bayern has named five goalkeepers as full-time club captain.

   a.  True
   b.  False

# QUIZ ANSWERS

1. B – 16

2. A – True

3. D – Sepp Maier

4. D – 1979

5. D – Franz Beckenbauer

6. B – Philipp Lahm

7. A – True

8. D – 6

9. D – Stefan Effenberg

10. A – Manuel Neuer

11. C – Georg Schwarzenbeck

12. B – False

13. B – Raimond Aumann

14. B – 3

15. D – Karl-Heinz Rummenigge

16. B – False

17. C – Mark van Bommel

18. C – Lothar Matthäus

19. A – Thomas Müller

20. B – False

# DID YOU KNOW?

1.  Since joining the Bundesliga in 1965, Bayern Munich has had 16 full-time captains: 1965-1970, Werner Olk; 1970-1977, Franz Beckenbauer; 1977-1979, Sepp Maier; 1979, Gerd Müller; 1979-1980, Georg Schwarzenbeck; 1980-1983, Paul Breitner; 1983-1984, Karl-Heinz Rummenigge; 1984-1991, Klaus Augenthaler; 1991-1994, Raimond Aumann; 1994-1997, Lothar Matthäus; 1997-1999, Thomas Helmer; 1999-2002, Stefan Effenberg; 2002-2008, Oliver Kahn; 2008-2011, Mark van Bommel; 2011-2017, Philipp Lahm; and the current skipper since 2017 is Manuel Neuer.

2.  Bayern has had four goalkeepers serve as full-time captain since 1965. They are Sepp Maier, Raimond Aumann, Oliver Kahn, and current captain Manuel Neuer. Sixteen of the 17 captains have hailed from Germany. The only non-German skipper was former Dutch international midfielder Mark van Bommel, who was born in Maasbracht, Holland.

3.  Mark van Bommel arrived in Bayern from Barcelona in August 2006 for €6 million. He was named the club's Player of the Year for his play in 2006-07 and helped the squad win the League and German Cup double the next season. He then took over as team captain in 2008 when former skipper Oliver Kahn announced his retirement. Van Bommel then led Bayern to another league and cup

double in 2009-10, but the team's bid for a first treble was spoiled when Inter Milan beat them in the UEFA Champions League final. He then joined A.C. Milan on a free transfer in January 2011 after close to 200 appearances with Bayern.

4. One of the most famous Bayern captains before the Bundesliga era was Konrad "Conny" Heidkamp, who joined the club in 1928-29. The German international left-back was nicknamed "Grenadier" because of his powerful shot, strong tackling, and precise passing skills. Heidkamp led the squad to the 1932 German championship, which was the team's first of many. During World War II, his wife Magdalena suggested the club should hide its collection of trophies in a crate buried on a farm to save them from bombing raids.

5. Midfielder Stefan Effenberg was regarded as a born leader, and he never failed to inspire and drive his teammates in the most challenging circumstances. Nicknamed "Cheffe," he was just 22 years old when arriving at Bayern in 1990 from Borussia Mönchengladbach. However, he left for Fiorentina after just two seasons. Bayern reacquired Effenberg from Borussia Mönchengladbach in 1998, and he went on to help the side claim three straight Bundesliga titles as well as the 2000 German Cup and the 2001 European Champions League and Club World Cup championships. He played 160 league games for Bayern with 35 goals before joining VfL Wolfsburg in 2002.

6. At one point, Klaus Augenthaler was the league's and club's most successful player when it came to collecting silverware. Augenthaler won a record seven league titles between 1979-80 and 1989-90 as well as three German Cups and two German Super Cups, and he also picked up a couple of European Cup Final runner-up medals. He was named to the Bundesliga Team of the Season on two occasions. The midfielder/defender, who captained the side from 1984 to 1991, played 404 league games with Bayern and scored 52 goals. He once scored from the halfway line to earn the 1989 Goal of the Season and Goal of the Decade Awards.

7. Energetic midfielder Paul Breitner served as captain between 1980 and 1983 during his second stint with the club. He started his pro career with Bayern from 1970 to 1974 before spending time with Real Madrid and Eintracht Braunschweig. Bayern reacquired him in 1978. He helped the team win the German Cup in 1971, three straight league titles starting in 1971-72, and the European Cup in 1974. After returning to Bayern in 1978, he won two more Bundesliga titles and another German Cup. Breitner's playing career ended in 1983 due to injury after notching over 80 goals in 255 league outings and winning several individual awards.

8. Defender Philipp Lahm won eight league titles, six German Cups, three DFL Super Cups, a League Cup, and one UEFA Champions League, UEFA Super Cup, and FIFA Club World Cup each with Bayern between 2002-03

and 2016-17. He also played over 500 games with the club and wore the captain's armband between 2011 and 2017. Lahm was known as "Mr. Reliable" on and off the pitch and spent more than 20 years of his life with Bayern, usually as a fullback or midfielder.

9. A total of 16 of Bayern's 17 captains since 1965 played internationally for their homeland. The only one who didn't was the club's last captain before the team was promoted to the Bundesliga in 1965, defender Adolf Kunstwadl. The team's first Bundesliga skipper, Werner Olk, played just one match for West Germany in 1961 while goalkeeper Raimond Aumann played four times with West Germany between 1989 and 1990.

10. Of the full-time captains since 1965, seven also served as captains of the West German or unified national team at one time or another. They were Franz Beckenbauer, Sepp Maier, Karl-Heinz Rummenigge, Lothar Matthäus, Oliver Kahn, Phillip Lahm, and Manuel Neuer. Beckenbauer led the squad to the 1972 European Championship and 1974 World Cup titles, while Matthäus guided the team to the 1990 World Cup, and Lahm led them to the 2014 World Cup. Matthäus was also the first skipper of the unified German national team when East and West Germany united in 1990.

# CHAPTER 3:

# AMAZING MANAGERS

## QUIZ TIME!

1. Who was Bayern's first manager in the Bundesliga era?

    a. Branko Zebec

    b. Dettmar Cramer

    c. Zlatko Čajkovski

    d. Udo Lattek

2. From 1902 to 1963, Bayern had approximately 30 managers.

    a. True

    b. False

3. As of 2020, who is Bayern's most decorated Bundesliga manager?

    a. Pep Guardiola

    b. Ottmar Hitzfeld

    c. Jupp Heynckes

    d. Udo Lattek

4. In 1977, after a lackluster year, Bayern swapped manager Dettmar Cramer to which Bundesliga club in return for Gyula Lóránt?

    a. Bayer Leverkusen
    b. FC Schalke 04
    c. Eintracht Frankfurt
    d. Hertha BSC

5. Who was appointed manager on July 1, 2009?

    a. Jürgen Klinsmann
    b. Jupp Heynckes
    c. Andries Jonker
    d. Louis van Gaal

6. On November 3, 2019, Bayern parted ways with which manager following a 5-1 defeat to Eintracht Frankfurt?

    a. Niko Kovač
    b. Jupp Heynckes
    c. Willy Sagnol
    d. Carlo Ancelotti

7. Between 2000 and 2010, Bayern had five different managers, including caretakers.

    a. True
    b. False

8. How many spells did Jupp Heynckes have as Bayern's manager, including caretaker appointments?

    a. 2
    b. 3

c. 4

d. 5

9. Who managed Bayern in 1994-95?

    a. Franz Beckenbauer

    b. Klaus Augenthaler

    c. Otto Rehhagel

    d. Giovanni Trapattoni

10. How many full-time managers has the club had between 2017 and 2020?

    a. 3

    b. 7

    c. 6

    d. 5

11. How many months did Søren Lerby manage the club?

    a. 2

    b. 5

    c. 10

    d. 20

12. Hans-Dieter Flick won the FIFA Football Coach of the Year award after his first season managing Bayern in 2019-20.

    a. True

    b. False

13. How many Bundesliga titles did Ottmar Hitzfeld win with Bayern?

    a. 3

    b. 4

c. 5

d. 6

14. Before joining Bayern in 1994, Giovanni Trapattoni managed which famous club?

    a. A.C. Milan

    b. Inter Milan

    c. S.L. Benfica

    d. Juventus

15. Before he came to Bayern, which Spanish club did Pep Guardiola manage?

    a. Sevilla FC

    b. Real Madrid

    c. FC Barcelona

    d. Athletic Bilbao

16. Bayern has appointed just three caretaker-managers in the Bundesliga as of 2020.

    a. True

    b. False

17. Who managed Bayern from July 2013 to June 2016?

    a. Willy Sagnol

    b. Pep Guardiola

    c. Carlo Ancelotti

    d. Andries Jonker

18. What club did Felix Magath manage before he came to Bayern?

a. Werder Bremen

b. VfL Wolfsburg

c. FC Schalke 04

d. VfB Stuttgart

19. How many German Cups (DFB-Pokal) did Ottmar Hitzfeld win as Bayern manager?

    a. 0

    b. 2

    c. 3

    d. 5

20. In Udo Lattek's first stint as manager (1970-75), the club allowed 278 goals in Bundesliga matches, the most allowed by a Bayern manager in a stint with the club.

    a. True

    b. False

# QUIZ ANSWERS

1. C – Zlatko Čajkovski

2. A – True

3. B – Ottmar Hitzfeld

4. C – Eintracht Frankfurt

5. D – Louis van Gaal

6. A – Niko Kovač

7. B – False

8. C – 4

9. D – Giovanni Trapattoni

10. A – 3

11. B – 5

12. B – False

13. C – 5

14. D – Juventus

15. C – FC Barcelona

16. B – False

17. B – Pep Guardiola

18. D – VfB Stuttgart

19. C – 3

20. B – False

# DID YOU KNOW?

1. It's believed that Bayern Munich employed approximately 30 different full-time managers between the club's inception in 1900 and 1963, when the German Bundesliga was born. The first full-time manager is believed to have been Dr. Willem Hesselink of Holland between 1902 and 1905.

2. Richard Kohn was the first manager to win the league title with the club in 1932. The native of Vienna, Austria, was also known by his nickname Dombi or Little Dombi as well as aliases such as John Little, Jack Domby, and Ricardo Domby. The former player managed the club from 1931 to 1933 before leaving for Barcelona in Spain when the Nazis gained more power.

3. Since 1963, when the German Bundesliga was formed, Bayern Munich has employed 27 different and 31 combined managers and caretaker-managers. This includes managers who have taken over the club for two or more stints, such as Udo Lattek, Giovanni Trapattoni, Franz Beckenbauer, Ottmar Hitzfeld, and Jupp Heynckes. In fact, Heynckes has been in charge of the team on three different occasions: April 28 to June 30, 2009, as caretaker; July 1, 2011, to June 30, 2013; and from October 9, 2017, to June 30, 2018.

4. As of 2020, four Bayern managers have won the German Football Manager of the Year Award. They were Felix Magath in 2005, Ottmar Hitzfeld in 2008, Louis van Gaal in 2010, and Jupp Heynckes in 2013 and again in 2018. Hitzfeld was awarded the UEFA Coach of the Year honors in 2001, along with the IFFHS World's Best Club Coach Award. In addition, Heynckes took home the FIFA World Coach of the Year and the IFFHS World's Best Club Coach Awards for 2013.

5. The longest-serving Bayern manager has been Ottmar Hitzfeld, who was in charge of the squad for a total of 2,706 days. He was in charge from July 1, 1998, to June 30, 2004, and then again from February 1, 2007, to June 30, 2008. As of 2020, Hitzfeld was one of just five soccer managers to win the European Cup/UEFA Champions League with two different teams; former Bayern bosses Jupp Heynckes and Carlo Ancelotti are the other two. Hitzfeld managed close to 500 games with the team. His winning percentage was 60.50 in his first stint and 59.21 in his second stint.

6. Manager Dettmar Cramer was extremely successful in Europe with Bayern but not so much in domestic competitions. He took over on January 16, 1975, and remained until November 30, 1977, winning two straight European Cups in 1975 and 1976, as well as the Club World Cup in 1976. However, his Bundesliga record was a mediocre 40 wins, 27 draws, and 34 losses in 101 games, and he didn't win any domestic silverware. Cramer's overall winning percentage with the team was 46.32.

7. The shortest stint for a non-caretaker manager was just 153 days for Søren Lerby from October 9, 1991, to March 10, 1992. He was in charge for just 17 matches and had a record of five wins, five draws, and seven defeats for a winning percentage of 29.41. Lerby, of Copenhagen, Denmark, played with the club as a midfielder between 1983 and 1986 and helped Bayern win two league titles and German Cups. After he was replaced as manager, Lerby became a licensed sports agent.

8. Bayern's first manager in the Bundesliga was Zlatko Čajkovski, who was born in Zagreb, in the nation now known as Croatia. Čajkovski was hired on July 1, 1963, and stayed with the club until June 30, 1968. He won two German Cups with the side as well as a UEFA Cup Winners' Cup in 1967. The former international player coached in Israel, Turkey, and Holland before joining Bayern, but was coaching in Germany with FC Köln directly before heading to Munich. In just over 100 games with Bayern, Čajkovski's winning percentage was 50.98.

9. One of the most famous Bayern managers of the modern era was Pep Guardiola of Spain, who ran the club from July 1, 2013, to June 30, 2016. The former Barcelona midfielder made a name for himself managing the Spanish club from 2008 to 2012 and hauling in a very impressive amount of silverware. With Bayern, Guardiola captured three league titles, two German Cups, a UEFA Super Cup, and a FIFAS Club World Cup while boasting a winning

percentage of 75.16. He then left for Manchester City where he was still managing as of January 2021.

10. Another well-known recent manager with Bayern was Carlo Ancelotti of Italy, who was with the team from July 1, 2016, to September 28, 2017. The former midfielder had already managed famous clubs such as Juventus, A.C. Milan, Chelsea, Paris Saint-Germain, and Real Madrid and had won the European Champions League twice with Milan and once with Real Madrid. He won the Bundesliga in 2016-17 with Bayern along with the 2016 and 2017 German Super Cup and posted a 70.00 percent winning record with the team. However, he was fired after losing 3-0 away to Paris Saint-Germain in a Champions League group match.

# CHAPTER 4:

# GOALTENDING GREATS

## QUIZ TIME!

1. What year did Bayern acquire Manuel Neuer?

    a. 2010

    b. 2011

    c. 2012

    d. 2013

2. Jean-Marie Pfaff was the first winner of the IFFHS World's Best Goalkeeper award in 1987.

    a. True

    b. False

3. How many matches did Sven Scheuer play as Oliver Kahn's backup in all competitions in 1994-95?

    a. 9

    b. 10

    c. 12

    d. 14

4. Which keeper received a red card in 2000-01?

    a. Stefan Wessels
    b. Oliver Kahn
    c. Bernd Dreher
    d. Michael Rensing

5. How many Bundesliga appearances did Sepp Maier make with Bayern?

    a. 510
    b. 473
    c. 577
    d. 602

6. Which keeper made approximately 150 appearances for Bayern in domestic league matches?

    a. Hans-Jörg Butt
    b. Manfred Müller
    c. Jean-Marie Pfaff
    d. Walter Junghans

7. Sepp Maier was Bayern's first choice as keeper when the club entered the Bundesliga.

    a. True
    b. False

8. Which keeper played 1,462 minutes in 1991-92 domestic league games?

    a. Harald Schumacher
    b. Sven Scheuer
    c. Raimond Aumann
    d. Gerald Hillringhaus

9. Tom Starke played 10 Bundesliga matches with Bayern and won how many of them?

    a. 0

    b. 2

    c. 6

    d. 10

10. Which Bayern keeper won the IFFHS World's Best Goalkeeper award in four consecutive years?

    a. Manuel Neuer

    b. Oliver Kahn

    c. Sepp Maier

    d. Raimond Aumann

11. This keeper played 3,060 minutes in 1988-89.

    a. Harald Schumacher

    b. Uwe Gospodarek

    c. Gerald Hillringhaus

    d. Raimond Aumann

12. Keeper Pepe Reina won 10 games for Bayern in 2014-15 league matches.

    a. True

    b. False

13. Which keeper won 19 Bundesliga matches in 2009-10?

    a. Michael Rensing

    b. Thomas Kraft

    c. Hans-Jörg Butt

    d. Oliver Kahn

14. When did Sepp Maier win his first German Footballer of the Year award with Bayern?

    a. 1978

    b. 1977

    c. 1975

    d. 1973

15. How many Bundesliga matches did Hans-Jörg Butt end with a clean sheet in 2010-11?

    a. 5

    b. 6

    c. 7

    d. 8

16. Manuel Neuer has been dubbed the "sweeper-keeper" because of his tendency to play the ball outside of the 18-yard box.

    a. True

    b. False

17. Where did Sepp Maier rank in voting for the IFFHS World's Goalkeeper of the Century award?

    a. 4th

    b. 5th

    c. 6th

    d. 8th

18. How many times did Oliver Kahn win the IFFHS World's Best Goalkeeper award?

    a. 1

    b. 2

c. 3

d. 4

19. Which keeper played 29 Bundesliga matches in 2017-18?

    a. Sven Ulreich

    b. Tom Starke

    c. Ron-Thorben Hoffmann

    d. Leo Weinkauf

20. In 2001 and 2002, Oliver Kahn finished second in voting for the Ballon d'Or.

    a. True

    b. False

# QUIZ ANSWERS

1. B – 2011

2. A – True

3. D – 14

4. B – Oliver Kahn

5. B – 473

6. C – Jean-Marie Pfaff

7. A – True

8. D – Gerald Hillringhaus

9. D – 10

10. A – Manuel Neuer

11. D – Raimond Aumann

12. B – False

13. C – Hans-Jörg Butt

14. C – 1975

15. B – 6

16. A – True

17. A – 4th

18. C – 3

19. A – Sven Ulreich

20. B – False

# DID YOU KNOW?

1. Goalkeeper Sepp Maier served as team captain between 1977 and 1979 and holds several club records, including the most appearances for the club with approximately 700, the most league appearances at 537, the most Bundesliga matches at 473, the most German Cup contests with 63, and the most consecutive games in the Bundesliga at 442 between 1966 and 1979. Maier played with the squad his entire career from 1962 to 1980 and was named German Footballer of the Year for 1975, 1977, and 1978. He also helped Bayern win four Bundesliga titles and German Cups with three straight European Cups, a European Cup Winners' Cup, and an Intercontinental Cup.

2. Another goalkeeper who skippered Bayern was Oliver Kahn, who wore the armband between 2002 and 2008. Khan hated losing and supporters could easily see that because he would often berate his own players while taking charge of the 18-yard box. He signed with Bayern in 1994 and stayed until retiring in 2008, playing just over 630 games with the side. Khan helped his teammates capture eight league titles, a record six German Cups, five League Cups, a Champions League crown, an Intercontinental Cup, and a UEFA Cup. Khan also won numerous individual awards and was known as a fearless goalie who never thought twice about charging off of his goal line to confront opposing attackers.

3. Raimond Aumann tended goal for Bayern from 1982 to 1994 and wore the captain's armband between 1991 and 1994. He then spent the last season of his pro career with Beşiktaş in Turkey. Nicknamed "Balu," Aumann played over 200 games with Bayern, winning six league titles and a pair of German Cups and German Super Cups. He also won a runner-up medal for the 1986-87 European Cup, when Porto of Portugal erased a 1-0 deficit with two goals in the final 12 minutes to win 2-1 in Vienna.

4. Jean-Marie Pfaff was a Belgian international keeper who joined Bayern in 1982 from Beveren in his homeland. He had already been named the best footballer in the Belgian First Division and had won a league title and Belgian Cup there when he headed to Munich. He would continue to rack up the silverware in the Bundesliga by helping Bayern win three straight league titles, starting in 1984-85, and a pair of German Cups. Pfaff was considered by many to be Belgium's greatest keeper and one of the finest in the world.

5. After his playing career ended, Walter Junghans became a goaltending coach and worked with Bayern Munich II and the club's under-19 team. Junghans began his pro career with Bayern between 1987 and 1992, when he was number two to Sepp Maier. He was on the side that won two league titles and a German Cup before he left for Schalke 04. Although never capped for Germany, he did play a couple of games with the West German Olympic squad in 1983-84.

6. By the time Hans-Jörg Butt arrived at Bayern in 2008 from Benfica in Portugal, he was already 34 years old. He stayed with the team until 2012 and played in over 60 games, also making four appearances with the German national side. Butt won the league title, German Cup, and German Super Cup in 2009-10 and Champions League runner-up medals in 2009-10 and 2011-12. Butt was a penalty-taking specialist and scored 29 goals in his league career, one of them for Bayern, and a total of 26 in the Bundesliga overall.

7. Manfred Müller was with Bayern between 1979 and 1984 as a backup keeper. He played approximately 50 league games over that time. He joined from ESV Ingolstadt and helped Bayern win two straight league crowns in 1979-80 and 1980-81 as well as German Cups in 1981-82 and 1983-84. Müller was also a member of the runner-up side in the 1981-82 European Cup before leaving for 1. FC Nürnberg to become the club's general manager and emergency keeper.

8. Michael Rensing joined the club in 2000 from TuS Lingen and was developed with Bayern's youth teams. He played twice for the reserve squad in the 2001-02 season and played in the Regionalliga Süd league in 2002-03. The next season he became deputy to Oliver Kahn and made his first-team league debut in February 2004. He played nearly 100 league games with Bayern and was on the sides that won four league titles and German Cups as well as a League Cup. Rensing left in 2020 to join 1. FC Köln.

9. Current Hamburger SV goalkeeper Sven Ulreich played the previous five years, from 2015 to 2020, with Bayern, playing in 70 contests. Before that, he was with VfB Stuttgart for almost a decade. He saw most of his action with Bayern in 2017-18, when number one keeper Manuel Neuer was injured, and he got into 47 games. Ulreich helped the squad win five straight league titles during his stay, along with three consecutive German Super Cups, three German Cups, a European Champions League crown, and a UEFA Super Cup.

10. Goalkeeper Manuel Neuer was made team captain in 2017 and has also skippered the German national team like fellow keepers Sepp Maier and Oliver Kahn. Neuer joined Bayern from Schalke 04 in 2011, which caused an uproar among some Bayern fans. He soon won them over, though, by setting a new club record, playing more than 1,000 straight minutes without allowing a goal, which broke the old mark set by Oliver Kahn. Neuer posted his 200th clean sheet for the team in his 394th outing in October 2020, and he has helped them win eight straight league titles as well as five German Cups and German Super Cups, two European Champions Leagues and UEFA Super Cups, and a FIFA Club World Cup. He's also won numerous individual awards with the squad.

# CHAPTER 5:

# DARING DEFENDERS

## QUIZ TIME!

1. Which defender wore number 69?

    a. Lúcio

    b. Robert Kovač

    c. Thomas Linke

    d. Bixente Lizarazu

2. Philip Lahm scored 25 goals in domestic league matches with Bayern.

    a. True

    b. False

3. Approximately how many appearances did Franz Beckenbauer make in all competitions with Bayern?

    a. 300

    b. 400

    c. 500

    d. 600

4. Which of these defenders scored four goals in the 2016-17 Bundesliga season?

    a. Philip Lahm

    b. Juan Bernat

    c. David Alaba

    d. Javi Martínez

5. Who posted nine assists in all competitions in 2019-20?

    a. Alphonso Davies

    b. Benjamin Pavard

    c. Lucas Hernández

    d. Jérôme Boateng

6. Which defender played 2,896 minutes in 2011-12 domestic league matches?

    a. Jérôme Boateng

    b. Rafinha

    c. Holger Badstuber

    d. Daniel Van Buyten

7. Klaus Augenthaler was the first player to win seven Bundesliga titles.

    a. True

    b. False

8. How old was Norbert Eder when he joined Bayern in 1984?

    a. 17

    b. 18

    c. 29

    d. 32

9. Franz Beckenbauer won the Ballon d'Or in which two years?

  a. 1970 and 1973
  b. 1976 and 1977
  c. 1975 and 1978
  d. 1972 and 1976

10. Which defender scored six goals in the 2009-10 Bundesliga season?

  a. Holger Badstuber
  b. Daniel Van Buyten
  c. Diego Contento
  d. Edson Braafheid

11. This defender played his entire career with Bayern.

  a. Lúcio
  b. Olaf Thon
  c. Thomas Helmer
  d. Werner Olk

12. In 1999-2000, Samuel Kuffour was shown three red cards in domestic league matches.

  a. True
  b. False

13. How many Bundesliga titles did Udo Horsmann win with the club?

  a. 0
  b. 1
  c. 2
  d. 4

14. How many European Cups/Champions League titles did Klaus Augenthaler win with the team?

    a. 0
    b. 1
    c. 2
    d. 3

15. How many yellow cards did Willy Sagnol accumulate in the 2006-07 Bundesliga?

    a. 10
    b. 9
    c. 8
    d. 7

16. David Alaba won the Austrian Footballer of the Year award six consecutive times from 2011 to 2016.

    a. True
    b. False

17. Which nickname did Franz Beckenbauer earn because of his skill and ability with the ball?

    a. Der Maestro
    b. Der Kaiser
    c. Der Anmutige (The Graceful One)
    d. The King

18. Which defender finished second in voting for the 1981 Ballon d'Or?

    a. Hans Pflügler
    b. Udo Horsmann

c.  Kurt Niedermayer

d.  Paul Breitner

19. How many times did Franz Beckenbauer win the German Footballer of the Year award with Bayern?

a.  3

b.  4

c.  5

d.  6

20. Alphonso Davies was named the Bundesliga Rookie of the Season for 2019-20.

a.  True

b.  False

# QUIZ ANSWERS

1. D – Bixente Lizarazu

2. B – False

3. D – 600

4. C – David Alaba

5. A – Alphonso Davies

6. C – Holger Badstuber

7. A – True

8. C – 29

9. D – 1972 and 1976

10. B – Daniel Van Buyten

11. D – Werner Olk

12. B – False

13. C – 2

14. A – 0

15. C – 8

16. A – True

17. B – Der Kaiser

18. D – Paul Breitner

19. B – 4

20. A – True

# DID YOU KNOW?

1. German international Franz Beckenbauer was generally considered one of the world's greatest defenders, even though some thought he was a bit too robotic. To others, he was simply a genius, and this was the reason he won the European Player of the Year Award twice. The midfielder turned sweeper played with Bayern between 1964 and 1977 and helped the team hoist five league crowns, four German Cups, three straight European titles, a European Cup Winners' Cup, and an Intercontinental Cup. Beckenbauer, who was nicknamed "Der Kaiser," played just under 600 games with Bayern, scoring 70 goals, and he later managed the club as well as the German national team.

2. At just 5 feet 6 inches tall, French international left-back Bixente Lizarazu was still a giant among Bayern defenders. He was also one of the most successful, as he helped the squad win six league titles, five German Cups, four League Cups, an Intercontinental Cup, and the Champions League in 2000-01. Lizarazu was well known for his energy, athleticism, and professionalism on and off the pitch. He joined the team in 1997 from Athletic Bilbao in Spain and left in the summer of 2004 for French side Olympique Marseille. However, he returned to Bayern just six months later to finish his career.

3. German international defender Hans-Georg Schwarzenbeck was one of Bayern's most loyal and unsung players. He spent his entire career with the club from 1967 to 1981, appearing in 416 league games and another 70 in European competitions. Schwarzenbeck, who captained the side in 1979-80, helped his teammates collect six league titles, three German Cups, a European Cup, Winners' Cup, an Intercontinental Cup, and three straight European Champions League titles from 1974 to 1976. His late equalizer in extra time against Atlético Madrid in the 1974 European Cup Final sent the game to a replay for the first time in history, and Bayern won 4-0 just two days later.

4. Werner Olk was another ex-captain (1965-70) and defender who played his top-flight career with Bayern. Between 1960 and 1970, he helped the side win three German Cups, one Bundesliga title, and the European Cup Winners' Cup in 1967. Of course, he also helped Bayern earn promotion to the Bundesliga in the first place in 1965. Olk got into coaching and managing after hanging up his boots and enjoyed two spells with the club as an assistant from 1975 to 1977 and 1986 to 1988.

5. Being able to play both left- and center-back was a bonus for German international Hans Pflügler because it enabled him to play nearly 400 games with Bayern between 1981 and 1992 with a final appearance in 1995. He won five league titles, three German Cups, and a pair of German Super Cups in his career, and he chipped in with over 30

goals. Pflügler also played with Bayern's B squad in the 2001-02 campaign at the age of 42 before hanging up his boots.

6.  After joining from Borussia Dortmund in 1992, German international Thomas Helmer played with Bayern until leaving for Sunderland of England on a free transfer in 1999. He also captained the German side during his last two years in Munich. He helped the team capture three league titles and League Cups, along with a German Cup and UEFA Cup. Helmer played over 200 games with Bayern and worked as a journalist and broadcaster after retiring.

7.  Center-back Jérôme Boateng joined Bayern from England's Manchester City in 2011 and was still with the club in January 2021. The German international played as a youth with Tennis Borussia Berlin and then joined Hertha BSC in 2002 before ending up with Hamburger SV in 2007. Since joining Bayern, Boateng has helped the team lift eight straight league crowns, five German Cups, two German Super Cups, two European Champions League titles, a pair of UEFA Super Cups, and the FIFA Club World Cup. Boateng, the half-brother of footballer Kevin-Prince Boateng, was German Footballer of the Year for 2016-17 while being named to the Bundesliga Team of the Season twice.

8.  Samuel Kuffour was a Ghanaian international defender with tremendous power who played with Bayern from

1993 to 2005. Like most Bayern players, Kuffour won his fair share of trophies as he helped the club snag six league titles, four German Cups, two League Cups, the European Champions League, and the Intercontinental Cup. He was named the Ghana Player of the Year for 1998, 1999, and 2001 and the BBC African Footballer of the Year for 2001. Kuffour left for AS Roma of Italy in 2005 on a free transfer.

9.  German international defender Markus Babbel began his pro career with Bayern between 1991-92 before joining Hamburger SV. He was reacquired by Bayern in 1994 and remained with the club until heading to Liverpool in England in 2000. While in Munich, he won three league titles and League Cups, a pair of German Cups, and a UEFA Cup. Babbel retired in 2007 and got into management with stints in Germany, Switzerland, and Australia.

10. Johnny Hansen was a Danish international who joined Bayern in 1970 from 1. FC Nürnberg and stayed with the team until 1976, when he returned to his homeland to finish his career. The right-back helped Bayern capture three straight league titles and three consecutive European Cups. However, he missed the 1975 final due to illness. Hansen also won an Intercontinental Cup in 1976 and was named Danish Player of the Year in 1967 before heading to Germany to further his career.

# CHAPTER 6:

# MAESTROS OF THE MIDFIELD

## QUIZ TIME!

1. Which midfielder was nicknamed "Bulle"?

    a. Bastian Schweinsteiger

    b. Lothar Matthäus

    c. Hasan Salihamidžić

    d. Franz Roth

2. Bernd Dürnberger played his entire pro career with Bayern.

    a. True

    b. False

3. How many assists did Zé Roberto record in 2002-03 domestic league games?

    a. 10

    b. 9

    c. 8

    d. 7

4. This midfielder scored 14 Bundesliga goals in the 2005-06 campaign.

    a. Mehmet Scholl
    b. Owen Hargreaves
    c. Michael Ballack
    d. Sebastian Deisler

5. What nickname was Paul Breitner given by Bayern fans?

    a. The Revolution Man
    b. Der Afro
    c. The Boss
    d. Der Beard

6. Joshua Kimmich led the club with how many assists in the 2018-19 Bundesliga season?

    a. 9
    b. 10
    c. 13
    d. 15

7. Lothar Matthäus was the first midfielder on Bayern to win the German Footballer of the Year award in 1981.

    a. True
    b. False

8. Which midfielder won the Bravo Award in 2001?

    a. Markus Feulner
    b. Sebastian Deisler
    c. Hasan Salihamidžić
    d. Owen Hargreaves

9. Who was shown 11 yellow cards in the 2009-10 Bundesliga season?

   a. Martín Demichelis
   b. Mark van Bommel
   c. Bastian Schweinsteiger
   d. Hamit Altintop

10. Which player won the Golden Boy award in 2016?

    a. Joshua Kimmich
    b. Renato Sanches
    c. Corentin Tolisso
    d. Pierre Højbjerg

11. Which midfielder scored 10 Bundesliga goals in 2013-14?

    a. Mario Götze
    b. Pierre Højbjerg
    c. Xherdan Shaqiri
    d. Toni Kroos

12. Philippe Coutinho was the only club player to take a penalty kick in the 2019-20 Bundesliga.

    a. True
    b. False

13. Who tallied 10 assists in the 2011-12 Bundesliga?

    a. Luiz Gustavo
    b. Danijel Pranjić
    c. Takashi Usami
    d. Toni Kroos

14. Who was the only midfielder shown a red card in the 2000-01 domestic league?

    a. Michael Tarnat
    b. Jens Jeremies
    c. Hasan Salihamidžić
    d. Stefan Effenberg

15. Which midfielder had 10 Bundesliga goals in 1992-93?

    a. Christian Ziege
    b. Thomas Helmer
    c. Olaf Thon
    d. Jan Wouters

16. Mehmet Scholl scored five goals from penalty kicks in the 2000-01 Bundesliga.

    a. True
    b. False

17. How many games did Bastian Schweinsteiger play for Bayern?

    a. 318
    b. 337
    c. 342
    d. 500

18. Who played a total of 2,818 minutes throughout the 1997-98 Bundesliga season?

    a. Christian Nerlinger
    b. Thorsten Fink
    c. Dietmar Hamann
    d. Frank Gerster

19. Which midfielder played 2,288 minutes in 2016-17 domestic league matches?

    a. Xabi Alonso
    b. Joshua Kimmich
    c. Renato Sanches
    d. Thiago Alcántara

20. Bernd Dürnberger won 11 trophies with Bayern but was never called up to play for the German national team.

    a. True
    b. False

# QUIZ ANSWERS

1. D – Franz Roth

2. A – True

3. A – 10

4. C – Michael Ballack

5. B – Der Afro

6. C – 13

7. B – False

8. D – Owen Hargreaves

9. B – Mark van Bommel

10. B – Renato Sanches

11. A – Mario Götze

12. B – False

13. D – Toni Kroos

14. D – Stefan Effenberg

15. A – Christian Ziege

16. B – False

17. D – 500

18. A – Christian Nerlinger

19. D – Thiago Alcántara

20. A – True

# DID YOU KNOW?

1. Michael Ballack made a name for himself playing in Germany with Chemnitzer, Kaiserslautern, and Bayer Leverkusen before moving to Bayern in 2002. The German international was named German Footballer of the Year three times and netted 42 goals in 98 matches for Germany. He was a tremendous passer of the ball and also possessed a goalscorer's touch. With Bayern, he won three league titles and German Cups along with a League Cup. He also notched 62 goals in 157 outings before joining Chelsea on a free transfer in May 2006.

2. Lothar Matthäus was regarded as one of Germany's finest-ever midfielders. He starred for Borussia Mönchengladbach for five years before joining Bayern in 1984. However, he left four years later to sign with Inter Milan of Italy. Matthäus then rejoined Bayern from 1992 to 2000. He was named Germany's Player of the Year and Europe's Player of the Year twice each, and he won the first FIFA World Player of the Year award in 1991. Matthäus was known for his passing, tackling, versatility, and shooting and won seven league titles with Bayern along with three German Cups and League Cups, a German Super Cup, and a UEFA Cup.

3. French International Franck Ribéry graced the Bayern midfield for over 10 years and won a record nine

Bundesliga titles, six German Cups, four German Super Cups, a League Cup, a European Champions League, a UEFA Super Cup, and a FIFA Club World Cup. He played with Boulogne, Alès, Metz, Galatasaray, and Marseille before joining Bayern in 2007 for a then club record €25 million. Ribéry displayed tremendous dribbling skills, speed, and passing abilities, and his partnership with Arjen Robben was nicknamed "Robbery." Ribéry won several individual awards with Bayern and left for Fiorentina in Italy in 2019 after scoring 124 times in 425 matches.

4. Franz "Bulle" Roth was an instant hero with Bayern because the 21-year-old scored in stoppage to beat the Glasgow Rangers 1-0 in the 1967 European Cup Winners' Cup Final. He was hard, strong, and quick on the pitch and possessed a powerful shot that once saw him drive the ball right through the net against Rapid Vienna. He scored 72 times in 366 league games with the team from 1966 to 1978, even though his main role was to mark the opposition's top playmakers. Roth helped his side win four league titles and German Cups as well as three straight European Cups, a UEFA Cup Winners' Cup, and an Intercontinental Cup.

5. With 117 goals in 469 career matches with Bayern, German international Mehmet Scholl was a crowd favorite between 1992 and 2007. The popular player racked up numerous honors with the team and won a total of 21 trophies overall, including eight league titles, five German Cups and League Cups, a UEFA Cup, an Intercontinental Cup,

and a European Champions League. Scholl loved playing in Bavaria and turned down offers from Barcelona in 1996. After retiring, Scholl managed the Bayern Munich II side on two occasions between 2009 and 2013, and he also became a broadcaster.

6. Another fan favorite was solid German international Bastian Schweinsteiger, who started his youth career with the club in 1998 and didn't leave until 17 years later, when he joined Manchester United. He made his first-team debut as an 18-year-old and went on to tally 68 goals in exactly 500 appearances with the team. Schweinsteiger was on the receiving end of 20 team trophies, including eight league crowns, seven German Cups, a FIFA Club World Cup, a League Cup, a German Super Cup, a European Champions League, and a UEFA Super Cup. He won numerous individual awards and was German Footballer of the Year for 2013.

7. Hans-Dieter Flick was appointed Bayern manager in 2019, but from 1985 to 1990 he played over 100 times in the squad's midfield, scoring a handful of goals. He then played for 1. FC Köln until 1993 before hanging up his boots due to injuries in 2000 when he was with Germany's Victoria Bammental. Flick played for Germany's under-18 team but that's as far as he went internationally until working as an assistant manager with the senior side from 2006 to 2014. As a player with Bayern, Flick won four league titles, a German Cup, and a German Super Cup.

8. Playmaking German international Toni Kroos starred for Bayern's senior squad from 2007 to 2014 before he left for Real Madrid. Known for creativity, passing, set-pieces, and vision, he was just 17 years old when he made his first-team debut. He was then loaned to Bayer Leverkusen for 18 months before returning and becoming a Bayern regular. He won three league titles, two German Cups, a German Super Cup, a European Champions League, and a FIFA Club World Cup before leaving. He was also named to the Bundesliga Team of the Season three times.

9. Italian-born Spanish international Thiago Alcántara do Nascimento was known simply as Thiago to fans and fellow players. He played with Bayern from 2013 to 2020 after being acquired from Barcelona for €25 million. He helped the team win seven league titles in a row as well as the European Champions League, four German Cups, three German Super Cups, and a FIFA Club World Cup. This included a treble of the league, German Cup, and Champions League in 2019-20. Thiago, whose father Mazinho won the World Cup with Brazil in 1994, made the Bundesliga Team of the Season in 2016-17, and added 31 goals for Bayern in 235 outings.

10. Bernhard "Bernd" Dürnberger was a defensive midfielder who spent his entire pro career with Bayern from 1972 to 1985 and chipped in with 38 goals in 375 league contests and nine goals in 78 European outings. He helped the side win 11 major trophies, which consist of five league titles, two German Cups, an Intercontinental Cup, and three

consecutive European Cups from 1974 to 1976. Dürnberger never played for the national senior squad of Germany but did score once in five matches with the West German B team.

# CHAPTER 7:

# SENSATIONAL STRIKERS & FORWARDS

## QUIZ TIME!

1. How many Bundesliga goals did Gerd Müller score with Bayern?

    a. 382

    b. 365

    c. 350

    d. 327

2. In 2019-20, Thomas Müller set the Bundesliga record for the most assists in a season.

    a. True

    b. False

3. Who scored 162 goals in 310 Bundesliga games?

    a. Karl-Heinz Rummenigge

    b. Arjen Robben

    c. Dieter Hoeneß

    d. Roland Wohlfarth

4. Who led Bayern with 23 goals in the Bundesliga in 2003-04?

    a. Roy Makaay
    b. Claudio Pizzaro
    c. Roque Santa Cruz
    d. Paulo Guerrero

5. Who led the Bundesliga with 24 goals in 2007-08?

    a. Franck Ribéry
    b. Lukas Podolski
    c. Miroslav Klose
    d. Luca Toni

6. How many assists did Thomas Müller tally in the 2019-20 Bundesliga season?

    a. 19
    b. 20
    c. 21
    d. 22

7. Karl-Heinz Rummenigge won the Ballon d'Or in 1980, 1981, and 1983.

    a. True
    b. False

8. Who led Bayern and the Bundesliga with 21 goals in 2002-03?

    a. Claudio Pizzaro
    b. Giovane Élber
    c. Roy Makaay
    d. Alexander Zickler

9. Which member of Bayern did not lead the German national team in scoring in a World Cup tournament?

   a. Mario Gómez
   b. Thomas Müller
   c. Miroslav Klose
   d. Gerd Müller

10. How many goals did Gerd Müller score in Bayern's first Bundesliga season in 1965-66?

   a. 9
   b. 12
   c. 14
   d. 17

11. Which winger scored 12 goals in 2019-20 domestic league games?

   a. Kingsley Coman
   b. Ivan Perišić
   c. Philippe Coutinho
   d. Serge Gnabry

12. Joshua Zirkzee scored four goals in nine Bundesliga games in 2019-20.

   a. True
   b. False

13. Who scored 11 goals in the 1992-93 Bundesliga season?

   a. Bruno Labbadia
   b. Christian Ziege
   c. Roland Wohlfarth
   d. Michael Sternkopf

14. Which world record did Robert Lewandowski NOT set in a match against Wolfsburg on September 22, 2015?

    a. Most goals by a substitute
    b. Fastest hat trick
    c. Most goals scored with headers in a single game
    d. Fastest five goals in a match

15. How many domestic league goals did Arjen Robben score in 2014-15?

    a. 13
    b. 15
    c. 17
    d. 20

16. Gerd Müller was the first player in the Bundesliga to score 40 goals.

    a. True
    b. False

17. Which forward posted 11 goals and six assists in 2009-10?

    a. Luca Toni
    b. Ivica Olić
    c. Miroslav Klose
    d. Franck Ribéry

18. How many goals did Robert Lewandowski score in all competitions in 2016-17?

    a. 40
    b. 41
    c. 42
    d. 43

19. Which player recorded 14 assists in the 2012-13 Bundesliga season?

    a. Mario Mandžukić

    b. Arjen Robben

    c. Franck Ribéry

    d. Mario Gómez

20. When Uli Hoeneß retired, he ended his career with 100 goals in 239 domestic league matches.

    a. True

    b. False

# QUIZ ANSWERS

1. B – 365

2. A – True

3. A – Karl-Heinz Rummenigge

4. A – Roy Makaay

5. D – Luca Toni

6. C – 21

7. B – False

8. B – Giovane Élber

9. A – Mario Gómez

10. C – 14

11. D – Serge Gnabry

12. A – True

13. A – Bruno Labbadia

14. C – Most goals scored with headers in a single game

15. C – 17

16. A – True

17. B – Ivica Olić

18. D – 43

19. C – Franck Ribéry

20. B – False

# DID YOU KNOW?

1. By the time he was 27 years old, in 1979, Uli Hoeneß was already the club's general manager. But before that, he was one of the team's top strikers with 86 goals in his 239 league appearances. He starred with Bayern from 1970 to 1978 and collected three straight league titles, three consecutive European Champions League crowns, a FIFA Club World Cup, a German Cup, and an Intercontinental Cup. He retired at a young age due to injuries and later become the club's president. However, he pleaded guilty to tax evasion in 2014 and served 18 months in prison for the offense. Uli is the brother of former Bayern star Dieter Hoeneß.

2. Michael Rummenigge was always compared to older brother Karl-Heinz Rummenigge, and although he wasn't on the same level as the former Bayern captain, he was a fine player in his own right. Michael joined the club's youth system in 1981 and made his first-team debut in 1982-83. He scored 44 goals in 147 league games before leaving for Borussia Dortmund in 1988 and helped Bayern win three straight league titles, two German Cups, and a German Super Cup. Michael also played twice for the German national team.

3. Miroslav Klose was one of the top international strikers of his era. The Polish-born German international scored 71

goals in 137 games for his adopted homeland and also banged in over 300 club goals during his career. Bayern acquired Klose in June 2007 from Werder Bremen, and he played four years in Munich before joining Lazio in Italy. He scored 53 goals in 149 matches with Bayern while helping them win two League and German Cup doubles as well as a League Cup and German Super Cup.

4. Dutch international center forward Roy Makaay had an excellent strike rate during his career, with over 300 goals in 636 contests. He managed to tally 102 of those in 178 games with Bayern between 2003 and 2007. He arrived from Deportivo la Coruña in Spain for what was then a club-record fee of €18.75 million. He scored several crucial goals with the side before leaving for Feyenoord in his homeland. With Bayern, Makaay won two German Cup and League doubles as well as a League Cup.

5. Claudio Pizarro of Peru played for several big European clubs, including Werder Bremen and Chelsea, after leaving his homeland. He joined Bayern in 2001 from Werder Bremen and stayed until 2007, when he headed to Chelsea. Pizarro then returned to Bayern from Bremen in 2012 before once again going to Bremen three years later. Nicknamed the "Anden Bomber," Pizarro scored 125 goals for Bayern in 327 outings and helped the team win six league titles, five German Cups, a German Super Cup, a UEFA Super Cup, an Intercontinental Cup, and the European Champions League.

6. German international legend Jürgen Klinsmann was already a veteran when he joined Bayern in 1995 from Tottenham Hotspur, as he was past his 30th birthday. Klinsmann finished as the club's top scorer in 1995-96 and 1996-97 and knocked in a tournament-leading 15 goals in 12 games in the 1996 UEFA Cup to help Bayern hoist the trophy. He also won the league title with the team in 1996-97 before leaving. Klinsmann later managed Bayern from July 2008 to April 2009 after notching 48 goals in 84 matches as a player.

7. At 6 feet 4 inches tall, Carsten Jancker was an imposing figure on the pitch, but he also possessed a sublime touch for such a big man. After struggling to score at the start of his pro career, he joined Bayern in 1996 from Rapid Vienna, where he was on loan from 1. FC Köln. Jancker was partnered by Giovane Élber up front and began to flourish. He notched nearly 80 goals in just over 200 appearances for the squad and helped win four league titles and League Cups, along with two German Cups, an Intercontinental Cup, and the European Champions League. He left in 2002 to join Udinese in Italy.

8. German international Mario Gómez was one of the top scorers in the world when he played for Bayern between 2009 and 2013, scoring a goal for every 138 minutes played. He came over for a reported €35 million from Stuttgart, where he scored 87 goals in 156 games and was named German Footballer of the Year for 2007. Gómez then posted over 100 goals in fewer than 200 matches with

Bayern. He won the Bundesliga Golden Boot with 28 goals in 2010-11 and helped the side win two league titles, German Cups, and German Super Cups, as well as the European Champions League.

9. Italian international Luca Toni played with more than a dozen teams during his pro career. His stint at Bayern was relatively shot. He arrived in 2007 from Fiorentina in Italy and headed back to his homeland to play with Genoa in 2010. He had also been loaned to Roma in 2009. Toni scored 24 league goals in his first season to win the Bundesliga Golden Boot and was named to the Team of the Season. The club also won a domestic treble that campaign by capturing the league title, League Cup, and German Cup. Toni, who notched 58 goals in 89 games with Bayern, didn't see eye to eye with manager Louis van Gaal and was allowed to leave on a free transfer after his loan spell with Roma.

10. Mario Mandžukić was another forward whose time with Bayern was short but sweet, as he registered 48 goals in 88 games over just two seasons, leading the team in 2013-14 with 24 markers. He helped the team win the League and German Cup double in both campaigns, as well as a German Super Cup, UEFA Super Cup, European Champions League, and FIFA Club World Cup. Mandžukić, a Croatian international, joined from Wolfsburg for €13 million but left for Atlético Madrid just two years later because he didn't agree with manager Pep Guardiola's style of play.

# CHAPTER 8:

# NOTABLE TRANSFERS & SIGNINGS

## QUIZ TIME!

1. Which club was Robert Lewandowski playing for before signing with Bayern in 2014?

    a. Znicz Pruszków

    b. FC Schalke 04

    c. Borussia Dortmund

    d. Lech Poznań

2. Bayern signed Arjen Robben from English Premier League club Chelsea in 2008-09.

    a. True

    b. False

3. How much did Bayern reportedly sign Franck Ribéry for in 2007-08?

    a. €12 million

    b. €15 million

c. €20 million

d. €25 million

4. Which club did Lothar Matthäus get transferred to in 1999-2000 after his second stint with Bayern?

   a. Chicago Fire

   b. FC Herzogenaurach

   c. Inter Milan

   d. MetroStars

5. Who did Bayern sign from Karlsruher SC in 1994-95?

   a. Oliver Kahn

   b. Jean-Pierre Pappin

   c. Markus Babbel

   d. Alain Sutter

6. Which club did Roland Wohlfarth play for before joining Bayern in 1984-85?

   a. FC Bocholt

   b. VfB Leipzig

   c. MSV Duisburg

   d. AS Saint-Étienne

7. In 2012-13, Bayern signed Javi Martínez on a €38 million transfer.

   a. True

   b. False

8. Which French club did Bayern transfer Giovane Élber to in 2003-04?

a. Lyon

b. AS Monaco

c. Marseille

d. Stade Reims

9. Bayern signed which of these players on a free transfer in 1993-94?

a. Marcel Witeczek

b. Samuel Kuffour

c. Marco Grimm

d. Alexander Zickler

10. What was the reported transfer fee Bayern paid VfB Stuttgart in 2015-16 to acquire Joshua Kimmich?

a. €5 million

b. €7 million

c. €8.5 million

d. €10 million

11. Bayern signed which player from VfB Stuttgart in 2019-20?

a. Ivan Perišić

b. Leon Goretzka

c. Serge Gnabry

d. Benjamin Pavard

12. In 2009-10, Bayern signed Mario Gómez for what was then a record €20 million.

a. True

b. False

13. Which player did Bayern acquire from Hertha Zehlendorf in 1990-91?

    a. Christian Ziege
    b. Stefan Effenberg
    c. Brian Laudrup
    d. Michael Sternkopf

14. Bayern signed Michael Ballack from which Bundesliga club?

    a. Hannover 96
    b. Arminia Bielefeld
    c. Bayer Leverkusen
    d. VfL Wolfsburg

15. When Bayern signed Karl-Heinz Rummenigge in 1974, what approximate transfer fee did they pay to Borussia Lippstadt?

    a. €6,000
    b. €8,000
    c. €10,000
    d. €15,000

16. Bayern signed Alphonso Davies from the Vancouver Whitecaps for £17 million in 2018-19.

    a. True
    b. False

17. Who did Bayern sign from FK Austria Wien in 2008-09?

    a. Toni Kroos
    b. Diego Contento

c. Mehmet Ekici

d. David Alaba

18. Bayern's most expensive signing as of 2020 was Corentin Tolisso in 2017-18 for how a reported fee of how much?

    a. £45 million

    b. £41.5 million

    c. £38 million

    d. £37.5 million

19. Which of these players did Bayern loan to Roma in 2009-10?

    a. Luca Toni

    b. Mats Hummels

    c. Massimo Oddo

    d. Lúcio

20. In 2017-18, Bayern loaned Douglas Costa to Italian club Juventus.

    a. True

    b. False

# QUIZ ANSWERS

1. C – Borussia Dortmund

2. B – False

3. D – €25 million

4. D – MetroStars

5. A – Oliver Kahn

6. C – MSV Duisburg

7. B – False

8. A – Lyon

9. C – Marco Grimm

10. B – €7 million

11. D – Benjamin Pavard

12. B – False

13. A – Christian Ziege

14. C – Bayer Leverkusen

15. C – €10,000

16. A – True

17. D – David Alaba

18. B – £41.5 million

19. A – Luca Toni

20. A – True

# DID YOU KNOW?

1. Bayern picked up one of the best strikers in the history of the sport when they acquired Polish international Robert Lewandowski in January 2014 from rivals Borussia Dortmund. Remarkably, the club acquired the then 25-year-old on a free transfer. At the time, Lewandowski had already won the League and Polish Cups with Lech Poznań, along with two league titles, a German Cup, and a German Super Cup with Dortmund. And let's not forget he had won a Golden Boot with Dortmund and three in Poland earlier in his career. Lewandowski is currently the second-leading scorer all-time for Bayern and has won numerous individual and team awards with the club.

2. Defender Thomas Helmer was also acquired from Borussia Dortmund but in a more controversial manner. He signed with Dortmund in 1986 and spent six seasons with the club as a key player. Dortmund didn't want to sell Helmer to another German club in 1992 and therefore transferred him to Olympique Lyonnais in France. However, just three months later, Lyon suddenly sold Helmer to Bayern for a reported 7.5 million marks, which was a record transfer fee for Bayern. In addition, German national manager Berti Vogts thought about dropping Helmer from his 1992 European Championship squad due to the uproar and distraction that his transfer to Bayern was causing.

3. Midfield magician Arjen Robben was a bargain for Bayern as the Dutch international cost Real Madrid a reported €35 million when they bought him from Chelsea in 2007, and Bayern paid 10 million less for him two years later. Robben helped Real win a league title and Spanish Super Cup, but he became expendable when the club signed Kaká and Cristiano Ronaldo. Robben then went on to help Bayern win 20 pieces of silverware over the next decade and is one of the club's all-time top 10 scorers.

4. While Arjen Robben's move from Real Madrid to Bayern was successful, the same can't be said for Colombian international attacker James Rodriguez. In 2014, Real paid AS Monaco £63 million for Rodriguez basically due to his fine performance at that year's FIFA World Cup. He played three seasons with Real and helped the team win several trophies but scored just 36 goals. In July 2017, Bayern paid Real €13 million for Rodriguez on a two-year loan deal with the option to buy him for €42 million when the loan was up. He helped the squad win two league titles and a German Cup, but with just 15 goals in 67 games, Bayern felt he wasn't worth the money and was sent back to Spain in June 2019.

5. Another player Bayern took on loan from the Spanish La Liga was Brazilian international midfielder Philippe Coutinho. He forced a transfer from Liverpool to Barcelona in January 2018 for a reported fee of £105 million to £142 million, depending on various clauses being met. After just 76 games with the club, Coutinho was picked up on loan by

Bayern in August 2019 for a fee of €8.5 million plus the player's wages, which were a reported €25 million. Bayern also had the option of buying him for €120 million after the loan. Coutinho helped the team win a treble of the Bundesliga, German Cup, and European Champions League, with 11 goals in 38 outings and was then sent back to Barcelona at the end of the season.

6. It's apparent that English club Arsenal gave up too soon on German international winger Serge Gnabry. After Arsenal rarely played him between 2012 and 2016, Werder Bremen of Germany paid an approximate £5 million for his services in 2016, and he scored 11 goals in 27 league games. Bayern then paid €8 million for Gnabry in June 2017 and loaned him to Bundesliga rivals 1899 Hoffenheim for the season, where he scored 10 goals. Gnabry broke into Bayern's squad in 2018-19 and scored 41 times in his first 109 appearances. He's also been a hit at the national level, with six goals in six games for Germany's Olympic team and 14 goals in his first 17 appearances for the senior national side. By 2021, Gnabry had won two league titles and German Cups, a German Super Cup, a UEFA Super Cup, and the European Champions League with the club and was the team's Player of the Season in 2018-19.

7. Goalkeeper Manuel Neuer, the club's current captain as of January 2021, is a Bayern legend and one of the best keepers in the world, but many fans weren't happy upon his arrival. Neuer was team captain with Schalke 04 in 2010-11 and had been with the club since 2003, breaking

into the first team in 2006. However, with his contract due to expire, he decided to move on and was transferred to Bayern for a reported €18 million. Some Bayern supporters weren't thrilled that their club had bought a goalie from Schalke, but their tune soon changed with Neuer's remarkable play. By 2020, he had helped the club win 23 trophies, including eight straight league titles and two European Champions Leagues.

8. Portuguese international midfielder Renato Sanches appeared to be a future star due to his excellent performance at the 2016 European Championships. Bayern felt good about that since they signed him from Benfica of Portugal just a month earlier. They paid an initial fee of €35 million for the youngster, with a complicated add-on clause, which meant Sanches was the club's fourth-highest signing in history. He helped Bayern win the league in his first season but didn't record a goal or assist and rarely started. He was loaned to Swansea of the English Premier League the next season and failed to score again while playing just 15 times. Sanches would play just another 27 times with Bayern, scoring twice, before being sold to French club Lille for €25 million in August 2019.

9. While Mario Götze helped Bayern capture three straight league titles, two German Cups, a UEFA Super Cup, and a FIFA Club World Cup in his stint between 2013 and 2016, he seemed to be more at home at Borussia Dortmund. Bayern paid their rivals a release clause in Götze's contract of €37 million, which, at the time, made him the costliest

German player of all time. After 36 goals in 114 games, Bayern sold Götze back to Dortmund for a reported fee of €26 million. He then joined PSV Eindhoven in Holland in 2020 on a free transfer.

10. Striker Sandro Wagner joined Bayern back in 1995 as a youth and made his first-team debut a dozen years later. However, after fewer than 10 appearances he moved on to MSV Duisburg in 2008 and would then play with fellow German clubs Werder Bremen, 1. FC Kaiserslautern, Hertha BSC, Darmstadt 98, and 1899 Hoffenheim. He was reacquired by Bayern in January 2018 from Hoffenheim for a reported €12 million and would score 10 goals in 30 games before asking to be transferred due to lack of playing time. The German international striker was then sold for €5 million to Tianjin TEDA in China in January 2019 and retired in August 2020 at the age of 33.

# CHAPTER 9:

# ODDS & ENDS

## QUIZ TIME!

1. What year did Bayern move into Allianz Arena?

    a. 2004-05

    b. 2005-06

    c. 2006-07

    d. 2007-08

2. Between 2010 and 2019, Bayern won 138 of its 170 games on its home field.

    a. True

    b. False

3. The Der Klassiker is a famous clash between Bayern and which rivals?

    a. Borussia Dortmund

    b. TSV 1860 Munich

    c. FC Augsburg

    d. Bayer Leverkusen

4. Which of the following is not one of Bayern's nicknames?

    a. The Bavarians
    b. The Reds
    c. FC Hollywood
    d. The Red Menace

5. Who was the youngest player to make their debut for Bayern at the age of 17 years and 115 days?

    a. Pierre-Emile Højbjerg
    b. Jamal Musiala
    c. Toni Kroos
    d. David Alaba

6. Which player did NOT make the FIFPro XI in 2020?

    a. Robert Lewandowski
    b. Manuel Neuer
    c. Alphonso Davies
    d. Joshua Kimmich

7. Bayern had seven players on their roster win the 2014 World Cup with the German national team.

    a. True
    b. False

8. What was the final score of Bayern's biggest victory in the Bundesliga against Borussia Dortmund on November 27, 1971?

    a. 8-0
    b. 9-0
    c. 11-1
    d. 12-0

9. In 2000-01, Bayern set the record for the most losses in a season while winning the Bundesliga title, how many games did they lose?

    a. 8
    b. 9
    c. 10
    d. 11

10. Who made the most appearances for Bayern in the Oberliga Süd?

    a. Otto Schweizer
    b. Franz Bachl
    c. Jakob Streitle
    d. Hans Bauer

11. Which club did Bayern defeat 12-1 on aggregate in the UEFA Champions League in 2009?

    a. Lyon
    b. ACF Fiorentina
    c. FC Barcelona
    d. Sporting CP

12. In a match against Borussia Dortmund in 2001, Bayern were shown 15 yellow cards.

    a. True
    b. False

13. Bayern set a record for most points in a Bundesliga season in 2012-13, with how many?

    a. 89
    b. 90

c. 91

d. 92

14. How many league matches did Bayern draw in 1988-87?

    a. 15

    b. 14

    c. 13

    d. 12

15. Which team did Bayern suffer their biggest loss to in the Bundesliga era on October 9, 1976?

    a. Borussia Mönchengladbach

    b. FSV Mainz 05

    c. TSG 1899 Hoffenheim

    d. Schalke 04

16. When Bayern joined the Bundesliga in 1965-66, they set the record for most wins by a first-time Bundesliga team.

    a. True

    b. False

17. Who scored the fastest goal in a UEFA Champions League match in 10 seconds on March 7, 2007?

    a. Roy Makaay

    b. Claudio Pizarro

    c. Bastian Schweinsteiger

    d. Mark van Bommel

18. How many games did Bayern win in their debut season in the Bundesliga?

a. 18

b. 19

c. 20

d. 22

19. How many domestic league matches did Bayern lose in 2012-13?

    a. 4

    b. 3

    c. 2

    d. 1

20. In 2013-14, Bayern went a record 20 consecutive games unbeaten in the Bundesliga.

    a. True

    b. False

# QUIZ ANSWERS

1. B – 2005-06

2. A – True

3. A – Borussia Dortmund

4. D – The Red Menace

5. B – Jamal Musiala

6. B – Manuel Neuer

7. A – True

8. C – 11-1

9. B – 9

10. D – Hans Bauer

11. D – Sporting CP

12. B – False

13. C – 91

14. C – 13

15. D – Schalke 04

16. A – True

17. A – Roy Makaay

18. C – 20

19. D – 1

20. B – False

# DID YOU KNOW?

1. When Adolf Hitler gained more power in Nazi Germany in the late 1930s and early 1940s, Bayern Munich president Kurt Landauer and the team's manager both left the country as they were Jewish. At that time, Bayern was regarded as a Jewish club and ended up losing numerous fans to the neighboring TSV 1860 Munich football club.

2. Bayern Munich is known as the biggest sports club in all of Germany and one of the top-earning soccer enterprises in the world. The club also engages in other activities such as basketball, handball, table tennis, bowling, and even chess. Bayern also operates several women's soccer teams including a professional outfit that competes in the Frauen Bundesliga.

3. For most of Bayern's early days, the squad wore white and maroon kits at home. In the 1968-69 season, they changed to red-and-blue striped tops with blue shorts and socks. From 1969 to 1973, the home kits featured red-and-white striped shirts, white or red shorts, along with red socks. In 1973-74, they switched to an all-white kit with vertical blue-and-red stripes on the shirt. In 1974, the home kit changed to typically all red with white trim. The club experimented with different color schemes in the 1990s including a navy blue home kit that featured a red chest band.

4. There have been several versions of Bayern away kits over the years, which featured colors such as gold/green and

blue, white, and black. The club also has a used a different kit for international and European matches. Also, during the 1980s and 1990s, they wore a special away kit of blue and yellow when visiting 1. FC Kaiserslautern. This was similar to the Brazilian national kit, and it was born out of superstition as Bayern found it difficult to win at Kaiserslautern.

5.  Bayern's first friendly games were played in the center of Munich at the Schyrenplatz with official matches being contested at the Theresienwiese. The club's first home pitch came about in 1901 when they started to play at the Clemensstraße in Schwabing. When Bayern joined forces with the Münchner Sport-Club in 1906, they played at MSC's Leopoldstraße ground. However, when crowds grew larger in the 1920s, the team had to find various other pitches to play at in Munich.

6.  In 1925, the club moved in with their rivals TSV 1860 Munich and shared the Grünwalder Stadion ground with them. However, the 44,000-capacity stadium was damaged during World War II and had to be repaired following the conflict. The 79,000-capacity Olympiastadion was built for the 1972 Summer Olympics, and Bayern played their home games there from 1972 to 2005 before moving to Allianz Arena.

7.  In 2000, Bayern Munich and TSV 1860 Munich decided to erect a new home stadium, which could also be used to host the 2006 FIFA World Cup. The original capacity at Allianz Arena featured 66,000 seats that were fully covered

from the elements. The capacity has now been increased to 75,000, with the stadium being lit up in red for Bayern's home matches. In 2012, Bayern opened a museum in Allianz Arena displaying the history of the club, and the team's mascot, Berni, can also be found at the stadium.

8.  At home games, Bayern fans are known to sing a song named "Stern des Südens." They also used to sing "FC Bayern, Forever Number One" in the 1990s. Other songs are also popular with Bayern fans and may be heard at games, including "Mia san mia." This is a Bavarian variation of "Wir sind wir," which translates to "We are who we are" in English and is also the club's motto.

9.  The club is operated by FC Bayern München AG, which is a private company that isn't listed on a public stock exchange. Seventy-five percent of FC Bayern München AG is owned by the football club, with the remaining 25 percent being owned evenly by the Adidas, Audi, and Allianz companies, each of which owns 8.33 percent of the club's shares.

10. The club's training complex and headquarters is named Säbener Straße and can be found in Munich's borough of Untergiesing-Harlaching. Both the first team and reserve squad train there. The complex consists of five grass football pitches, with two of them featuring under-soil heating. There are also two artificial surface fields, as well as a multi-functional sports hall, beach volleyball court, a weight and fitness area, massage unit, library, conference room, restaurant, and family room.

# CHAPTER 10:

# DOMESTIC COMPETITION

## QUIZ TIME!

1. When did Bayern win their first national league title?

    a. 1931-32

    b. 1947-48

    c. 1968-69

    d. 1971-72

2. Bayern won their first German Cup (DFB-Pokal) in 1956-57.

    a. True

    b. False

3. Which club did Bayern defeat in the final round to win their first German Cup?

    a. Spandauer SV

    b. FC Saarbrücken

    c. Hamburger SV

    d. Fortuna Düsseldorf

4. Bayern beat which club 1-0 to win their last League Cup (DFB-Ligapokal) in 2007?

    a. VfB Stuttgart
    b. Werder Bremen
    c. FC Schalke 04
    d. FC Nürnberg

5. How many times has Bayern officially won the DFB/DFL German Super Cup as of 2020?

    a. 9
    b. 8
    c. 7
    d. 6

6. Who did Bayern defeat to win the 2005-06 German Cup?

    a. TSV 1860 Munich
    b. Eintracht Frankfurt
    c. FSV Mainz 05
    d. FC Erzgebirge Aue

7. Bayern has won the Bundesliga title a record eight consecutive years.

    a. True
    b. False

8. How many times did Bayern win the League Cup (DFB-Ligapokal)?

    a. 3
    b. 4
    c. 5
    d. 6

9. Bayern defeated which team 2-1 in the 2011-12 DFB/DFL German Super Cup final?

    a. Borussia Dortmund

    b. Werder Bremen

    c. Dresdner SC

    d. FC Köln

10. Who did Bayern play in its first German Cup final of the Bundesliga era?

    a. FC Kaiserslautern

    b. Meidericher SV

    c. Holstein Kiel

    d. Karlsruher SC

11. How many times has Bayern won the League and German Cup double as of 2020?

    a. 13

    b. 12

    c. 11

    d. 10

12. Bayern is the only Bundesliga team to win the League and German Cup double in back-to-back seasons on three separate occasions as of 2020.

    a. True

    b. False

13. Which side did Bayern defeat in the 2012-13 DFB/DFL German Super Cup final?

    a. Borussia Dortmund

    b. VfL Wolfsburg

c. VfB Stuttgart

d. SC Freiburg

14. Bayern Munich won the regional Bezirksliga Bayern competition a record number of times between 1923 and 1933. How many titles were won?

a. 4

b. 5

c. 6

d. 7

15. How many times has Bayern won the German Cup as of 2020?

a. 17

b. 18

c. 19

d. 20

16. Bayern has been runner-up to the league title a record nine times as of 2020.

a. True

b. False

17. Who did Bayern defeat to win their first DFB Super Cup in 1987?

a. FC Kaiserslautern

b. Hannover 96

c. Hamburger SV

d. Bayer Leverkusen

18. As of 2020, how many league titles has Bayern won?

    a. 26

    b. 29

    c. 30

    d. 34

19. Which club did Bayern NOT play against in the 1970-71 German Cup tournament?

    a. KSV Hessen Kassel

    b. FC Köln

    c. MSV Duisburg

    d. Borussia Mönchengladbach

20. Bayern won the DFB/DFL German Super Cup when it was first unofficially held in 1977.

    a. True

    b. False

# QUIZ ANSWERS

1. A – 1931-32

2. A – True

3. D – Fortuna Düsseldorf

4. C – FC Schalke 04

5. B – 8

6. B – Eintracht Frankfurt

7. A – True

8. D – 6

9. A – Borussia Dortmund

10. B – Meidericher SV

11. A – 13

12. A – True

13. C – VfB Stuttgart

14. D – 7

15. D – 20

16. B – False

17. C – Hamburger SV

18. C – 30

19. D – Borussia Mönchengladbach

20. B – False

# DID YOU KNOW?

1. Several domestic scoring records are held by the club's all-time leading scorer Gerd Müller, who was nicknamed "Der Bomber." He's the Bundesliga's all-time leading scorer with 365 goals in 427 games, and he scored on average once every 105 minutes to hold the record for players who have scored a minimum 20 goals. He holds the record for most goals in a Bundesliga season with 40 in 1971-72. Müller scored in a record 16 straight Bundesliga contests in 1969-70 and holds the record for two-goal games, with 87. He's also the current top scorer in German Cup games with 78 markers in 62 encounters, and he won a record seven Bundesliga Golden Boots.

2. As of 2020, seven different Bayern players had combined to win or share the Bundesliga Golden Boot 19 times. The following are the players, the seasons, and their goal totals: Gerd Müller—1966-67 (28), 1968-69 (30), 1969-70 (38), 1971-72 (40), 1972-73 (36), 1973-74 (30), 1977-78 (24); Karl-Heinz Rummenigge—1979-80 (26), 1980-81 (29), 1983-84 (26); Roland Wohlfarth—1988-89 (17), 1990-91 (21); Giovane Élber—2002-03 (21); Luca Toni—2007-08 (24); Mario Gómez—2010-11 (28); and Robert Lewandowski—2015-16 (30), 2017-18 (29), 2018-19 (22), 2019-20 (34).

3. Bayern has won a record 30 German league championships, with a record 29 of them coming in the Bundesliga. These

titles were won in 1932, 1968-69, 1971-72, 1972-73, 1973-74, 1979-80, 1980-81, 1984-85, 1985-86, 1986-87, 1988-89, 1989-90, 1993-94, 1996-97, 1998-99, 1999-2000, 2000-01, 2002-03, 2004-05, 2005-06, 2007-08, 2009-10, 2012-13, 2013-14, 2014-15, 2015-16, 2016-17, 2017-18, 2018-19, and 2019-20. The club also holds the record for runner-up in the Bundesliga on 10 occasions in 1969-70, 1970-71, 1987-88, 1990-91, 1992-93, 1995-96, 1997-98, 2003-04, 2008-09, and 2011-12.

4.  The record for German Cup (DFB-Pokal) championships is held by Bayern, with 20. They came in 1956-57, 1965-66, 1966-67, 1968-69, 1970-71, 1981-82, 1983-84, 1985-86, 1997-98, 1999-2000, 2002-03, 2004-05, 2005-06, 2007-08, 2009-10, 2012-13, 2013-14, 2015-16, 2018-19, and 2019-20. They were also the runner-up in 1984-85, 1998-99, 2011-12, and 2017-18.

5.  Bayern holds the record with eight German Super Cup triumphs, in 1987, 1990, 2010, 2012, 2016, 2017, 2018, and 2020. They also finished as runner-up a record six times, in 1989, 1994, 2013, 2014, 2015, and 2019. In addition, the former German League Cup, known as the DFL-Ligapokal, was contested between 1967 and 2007, with Bayern winning it a record six times in 1997, 1998, 1999, 2000, 2004, and 2007, while finishing as runner-up in 2006.

6.  The club holds numerous other Bundesliga records as of 2020. These include the most consecutive titles won, with eight from 2012-13 to 2019-20; the most games won, points accumulated, average points per game, and goals scored; the most consecutive wins at 19, the longest unbeaten streak at 53, and the most wins in a club's debut season

with 20. Bayern also won the title at the earliest date and with the most games remaining in a season, at seven. Their 25-point lead over the league runner-up in 2012-13 is a record, and the league victory of 11-1 over Borussia Dortmund in November 1971 is the league record.

7. Carrying on with the club's Bundesliga records, Bayern had the most points in a season, with 91, and the most wins, with 29. They had the fewest losses, just one; the most goals, 101; the fewest goals against, 17; the most clean sheets, 21; and the most consecutive victories to start a season, 10. On the darker side, Bayern's game versus Borussia Dortmund in 2000-01 resulted in a league-record 10 yellow and three red cards being shown. Bayern has won the most League and German Cup doubles at 13 and is the only German side to win a treble of the European Champions League, Bundesliga, and German Cup, which the club achieved in 2012-13 and 2019-20.

8. All players playing in the country are eligible for the German Footballer of the Year award. It was introduced in 1960 and has been won by the following Bayern players: Franz Beckenbauer (1966, 1968, 1974, 1976); Gerd Müller (1967, 1969); Sepp Maier (1975, 1977, 1978); Karl-Heinz Rummenigge (1980); Paul Breitner (1981); Lothar Matthäus (1999); Oliver Kahn (2000, 2001); Michael Ballack (2003, 2005); Franck Ribéry (2008); Arjen Robben (2010); Bastian Schweinsteiger (2013); Manuel Neuer (2014); Jérôme Boateng (2016); Philipp Lahm (2017); and Robert Lewandowski (2020).

9. Not everything has been rosy for Bayern in domestic competitions. The club has suffered a few humiliating losses at the feet of lower amateur teams. In the first round of the 1990-91 German Cup, Bayern traveled to FV Weinheim, which was playing in the Amateur-Oberliga Baden-Württemberg. Bayern's squad included six members of the 1990 German World Cup-winning team, but they were downed 1-0 and knocked out of the German Cup in the very first round for the first time in club history.

10. Bayern was beaten by lower division side FC Homburg in Munich in 1991, 4-2 in extra time. They also went home in the first round in 1994 to minnows TSV Vestenbergsgreuth, 1-0. However, during the same season, Bayern's reserve team beat Werder Bremen and VfB Stuttgart in the competition. More recently, on January 13, 2021, Bayern was beaten 6-5 in a penalty shootout away to Second Division club Holstein Kiel in a shocker after the game ended in a 2-2 draw.

# CHAPTER 11:

# EUROPE & BEYOND

## QUIZ TIME!

1. How many times has Bayern won the UEFA Champions League as of 2020?

    a. 4
    b. 5
    c. 6
    d. 7

2. Bayern has won two international trebles as of 2020.

    a. True
    b. False

3. Which club did Bayern defeat to win its first UEFA Champions League in 1973-74?

    a. Red Star Belgrade
    b. Celtic FC
    c. Atlético Madrid
    d. Újpesti Dózsa

4. How many times did Bayern win the Inter-Cities Fairs Cup?

   a. 3

   b. 2

   c. 1

   d. 0

5. Bayern defeated which French club to win its first UEFA Europa League Cup in 1995-96?

   a. Lyon

   b. Bordeaux

   c. Paris Saint-Germain

   d. RC Lens

6. Who did Bayern defeat in the 1966-67 UEFA Cup Winners' Cup?

   a. Servette FC

   b. Standard Liège

   c. PFC Slavia Sofia

   d. Rangers FC

7. Bayern holds the record for most UEFA Champions League titles won by a German team.

   a. True

   b. False

8. When did Bayern reach the quarterfinals of the Inter-Cities Fairs Cup for the first time?

   a. 1961-62

   b. 1962-63

c.  1963-64

d.  1964-65

9.  Who did Bayern face off against in the 2013 UEFA Super Cup final?

   a.  Real Madrid

   b.  Chelsea

   c.  Manchester United

   d.  Sevilla FC

10. When did Bayern win its first Intercontinental Cup?

   a.  1973

   b.  1974

   c.  1975

   d.  1976

11. Which club beat Bayern in the 2009-10 UEFA Champions League final?

   a.  Inter Milan

   b.  Chelsea

   c.  Barcelona

   d.  Juventus

12. The 1974 UEFA Super Cup final between Bayern and 1. FC Magdeburg was not held because neither team could come to terms on when to hold the match.

   a.  True

   b.  False

13. As of 2020, how many times has Bayern won the UEFA Super Cup?

a. 1

b. 2

c. 3

d. 4

14. Bayern defeated which club to win its first international treble in 2012-13?

    a. Real Madrid

    b. Paris Saint-Germain

    c. FC Barcelona

    d. Borussia Dortmund

15. What year was Bayern NOT a runner-up for the UEFA Super Cup?

    a. 1975

    b. 1976

    c. 2001

    d. 2017

16. Bayern is the only German team to win the FIFA Club World Cup twice.

    a. True

    b. False

17. How many international championships has Bayern won as of 2020?

    a. 11

    b. 12

    c. 13

    d. 14

18. Bayern defeated which club to win the 2013 FIFA Club World Cup?

    a. Raja Casablanca

    b. Auckland City FC

    c. Atlético Mineiro

    d. Guangzhou Evergrande TFC

19. How many times has Bayern lost in the UEFA Champions League final?

    a. 3

    b. 4

    c. 5

    d. 6

20. Bayern has been runner-up in the UEFA Super Cup five times as of 2020.

    a. True

    b. False

# QUIZ ANSWERS

1. C – 6

2. A – True

3. C – Atlético Madrid

4. D – 0

5. B – Bordeaux

6. D – Rangers FC

7. A – True

8. B – 1962-63

9. B – Chelsea

10. D – 1976

11. A – Inter Milan

12. A – True

13. B – 2

14. D – Borussia Dortmund

15. D – 2017

16. B – False

17. C – 13

18. A – Raja Casablanca

19. C – 5

20. B – False

# DID YOU KNOW?

1. Bayern has won numerous international titles and, as of 2020, was one of just five clubs to win all three major European competitions; the European Cup/Champions League, the UEFA Cup/Europa League, and the Inter-Cities Fairs Cup/European/UEFA Cup Winners' Cup. Bayern is also one of only three teams to win the European Cup/Champions League three years in a row (1974-76). The club has been crowned European champion six times to set a record for German clubs and has been runner-up five times. Bayern won the championship in 1973-74, 1974-75, 1975-76, 2000-01, 2012-13, and 2019-20.

2. Bayern won the UEFA Cup/UEFA Europa League in 1995-96 and the European/UEFA Cup Winners' Cup in 1966-67. The club captured the European/UEFA Super Cup in 2013 and 2020 and reached the 1974 Super Cup final against 1. FC Magdeburg, but the game was canceled when the two teams couldn't agree on a suitable date to play the match. Bayern was also the runner-up in the Super Cup in 1975, 1976, and 2001. The team triumphed in the Intercontinental Cup in 1976 and 2001 and was a finalist in 1974 and 1975. However, the club refused to play in the tournament in 1974 and 1975. Atlético Madrid replaced them in 1974, while the event was canceled the next year. Bayern also won the 2013 FIFA Club World Cup.

3. The Intercontinental Cup was also known as the European/South American Cup and as the Toyota Cup between 1980 and 2004. The competition was endorsed by UEFA and CONMEBOL, and the winners of the UEFA Champions League would typically play the winner of the South American Copa Libertadores. The tournament was first played in 1960 and last contested in 2004. Between 1960 and 1979, the Intercontinental Cup was a two-legged tie. It then became a single-game final in 1980 and was played exclusively in Japan until the event ended in 2004.

4. The 2012-13 campaign was an unforgettable one for Bayern, which took the Bundesliga title and German Cup and capped off the season with the European Champions League. Bayern beat runner-up Borussia Dortmund by 25 points to capture the league while losing just once during the season. The club clinched the German Cup with a 3-2 decision over VfB Stuttgart and triumphed in Europe with a 2-1 victory over their old rivals Borussia Dortmund. This dramatic treble came courtesy of a last-minute Champions League winner by Arjen Robben, and Bayern repeated the feat in 2019-20.

5. One of Bayern's most heartbreaking European moments came in the 1998-99 Champions League final against Manchester United in Barcelona. With a 1-0 lead and seemingly in control, Bayern hit the woodwork twice before falling apart. United manager Sir Alex Ferguson had sent on striker Teddy Sheringham in the 67th minute and Ole Gunnar Solskjaer 14 minutes later, hoping for an

unlikely comeback. Sheringham leveled the score 36 seconds into injury time, and Solskjaer scored the winner 101 seconds later against goalkeeper Oliver Kahn to give United the title.

6. Ivory Coast international striker Didier Drogba was a thorn in Bayern's side in the 2011-12 European Champions League final while playing for English side Chelsea. Drogba had endured some terrible moments in the tournament up until then, as he was sent off with a red card in the 2007-08 final against Manchester United and the next season was banned for three games after going ballistic when Chelsea was eliminated by Barcelona. He redeemed himself against Bayern, though, when Chelsea traveled to Munich for the 2012 final. With Chelsea behind 1-0 and just two minutes remaining, Drogba headed in the equalizer to send the contest to extra time. He then drilled home the winning penalty shot in a shootout to give Chelsea its first Champions League crown.

7. Gerd Müller leads the way as the most prolific club scorer in European games with 66 in 74 contests. As of January 2021, Robert Lewandowski had a team-high 54 goals in European Cup/UEFA Champions League matches and a club-record 15 goals in the 2019-20 Champions League season. The most UEFA Cup/UEFA Europa League and Inter-Cities Fairs Cup goals was scored by Jürgen Klinsmann, with 15, while the record for most UEFA Cup Winners' Cup goals belongs to Gerd Müller at 20. Müller also leads the club with three UEFA Super Cup tallies.

8. When it comes to international and European appearances while playing with Bayern, goalkeeper Oliver Kahn played a team-record 132 times and, as of January 2021, the most European Cup/UEFA Champions League appearances belonged to Thomas Müller at 123. The most UEFA Cup/UEFA Europa League and Inter-Cities Fairs Cup appearances was by Klaus Augenthaler, with 29. The most games in the UEFA Cup Winners' Cup competition belongs to goalkeeper Sepp Maier and Gerd Müller, with 25 each. Several players hold the mark for most UEFA Super Cup appearances: Franz Beckenbauer, Bernd Dürnberger, Udo Horsmann, Jupp Kapellmann, Sepp Maier, Karl-Heinz Rummenigge, and Hans-Georg Schwarzenbeck each played four games.

9. As of January 2021, Bayern held several records in European competition. The fastest goal in Champions League history was scored by Roy Makaay in just 10 seconds against Real Madrid in 2007. The club scored a minimum of two goals in each Champions League group stage games in 2010-11 and 2019-20. Also in 2019-20, Bayern became the first German team to win all six matches in the group stage of the Champions League. The club also owns the highest aggregate win in the knockout stage of the Champions League at 12-1 against Sporting CP in 2009. The biggest margin of victory in the knockout stage of the Champions League format was set at 7-0 against Basel in 2011-12.

10. Other records held by Bayern include the biggest victory in a quarterfinal during the Champions League era, when they downed FC Kaiserslautern 6-0 on aggregate in 1998-99, and again when they hammered Barcelona 8-2 in a single leg in 2019-20. The highest aggregate victory in a Champions League semifinal was 7-0 against Barcelona in 2012-13. In addition, the largest margin of victory in European Cup/Champions League final is 4-0 against Atlético Madrid in the 1973-74 replay. Bayern holds the Champions League record for 15 consecutive wins, 16 consecutive home wins, and seven straight away wins.

# CHAPTER 12:

# TOP SCORERS

## QUIZ TIME!

1. How many times has Robert Lewandowski led the Bundesliga in scoring with Bayern as of 2020?

    a. 5

    b. 4

    c. 3

    d. 2

2. Gerd Müller netted over 400 league goals combined with Bayern in the Bundesliga and the Regionalliga Süd.

    a. True

    b. False

3. Karl-Heinz Rummenigge led the team in scoring in how many seasons?

    a. 3

    b. 4

    c. 5

    d. 6

4. Who scored 42 goals in the Regionalliga Süd in 1964-65?

    a. Dieter Brenninger
    b. Gerd Müller
    c. Peter Grosser
    d. Rainer Ohlhauser

5. Which of these Bayern players has never won a Bundesliga Golden Boot award?

    a. Roland Wohlfarth
    b. Giovane Élber
    c. Luca Toni
    d. Roy Makaay

6. How many goals did Robert Lewandowski score in all competitions in 2019-20?

    a. 55
    b. 40
    c. 34
    d. 28

7. Lothar Matthäus led Bayern with the most domestic league goals in four consecutive seasons.

    a. True
    b. False

8. Where did Dieter Hoeneß rank in Bayern's all-time scoring list on January 1, 2021?

    a. 5th
    b. 6th
    c. 7th
    d. 8th

9. In 2014-15, Arjen Robben and Robert Lewandowski led Bayern in Bundesliga scoring, with how many goals?

    a. 18

    b. 17

    c. 16

    d. 15

10. Which two players were tied for the most league goals on the club with 11 in 1993-94?

    a. Christian Ziege and Lothar Matthäus

    b. Mehmet Scholl and Adolfo Valencia

    c. Christian Ziege and Bruno Labbadia

    d. Mehmet Scholl and Lothar Matthäus

11. Which player led Bayern with 18 league goals in 2013-14?

    a. Mario Gómez

    b. Claudio Pizarro

    c. Thomas Müller

    d. Mario Mandžukić

12. Thomas Müller has never led Bayern in goal scoring in a season as of 2020.

    a. True

    b. False

13. In which season did Gerd Müller score 40 Bundesliga goals?

    a. 1969-70

    b. 1970-71

    c. 1971-72

    d. 1972-73

14. Who was ranked the club's third all-time scorer as of January 1, 2021?

    a. Rainer Ohlhauser
    b. Arjen Robben
    c. Karl-Heinz Rummenigge
    d. Thomas Müller

15. In 1998-99, Giovane Élber and Carsten Jancker both scored how many league goals?

    a. 12
    b. 13
    c. 14
    d. 15

16. Karl-Heinz Rummenigge led the Bundesliga in scoring in four consecutive seasons.

    a. True
    b. False

17. How many Bundesliga Golden Boot awards did Gerd Müller win with Bayern?

    a. 3
    b. 5
    c. 7
    d. 8

18. How many times did Gerd Müller win the European Golden Boot?

    a. 0
    b. 1

c. 2

d. 4

19. How many goals did Roland Wohlfarth score in 1990-91 to lead the Bundesliga?

   a. 18

   b. 19

   c. 20

   d. 21

20. Robert Lewandowski scored a Bundesliga record 10 goals in the first five games of the 2020-21 season and 21 goals in the first 16 matches.

   a. True

   b. False

# QUIZ ANSWERS

1. B – 4

2. A – True

3. C – 5

4. D – Rainer Ohlhauser

5. D – Roy Makaay

6. A – 55

7. B – False

8. C – 7th

9. B – 17

10. B – Mehmet Scholl and Adolfo Valencia

11. D – Mario Mandžukić

12. A – True

13. C – 1971-72

14. C – Karl-Heinz Rummenigge

15. B – 13

16. B – False

17. C – 7

18. C – 2

19. D – 21

20. A – True

# DID YOU KNOW?

1. It's unclear exactly how many goals German international striker Gerd Müller scored for Bayern during his career from 1964 to 1979. But we do know he notched over 500 and is the all-time leading Bundesliga marksman with 365 markers in 427 appearances for a goals-per-game ratio of .85. Müller won four Bundesliga titles, four German Cups, three European crowns, an Intercontinental Cup, a UEFA Cup Winners' Cup, seven Bundesliga Golden Boots, and two European Golden Boots. He was also named European Footballer of the Year once and German Player of the Year twice. The former Bayern captain scored an incredible 68 times for Germany in 62 matches and holds several other club and national team scoring records.

2. Polish international striker Robert Lewandowski still has a way to go to catch Gerd Müller's team scoring record, but he's giving it his best shot. The prolific striker had reached the 270-goal mark by January 2021 while still playing with Bayern with over 180 goals in the Bundesliga. Lewandowski won three Golden Boots in Poland before signing in 2010 with Borussia Dortmund, where he won a Bundesliga Golden Boot. He signed with Bayern in 2014 and has won four more Golden Boots as well as numerous other individual awards, including the World Player of the Year for 2020. As far as team trophies go, Lewandowski has helped the squad win six straight league titles, four

German Super Cups, a Champions League, and a UEFA Super Cup.

3. Center forward Karl-Heinz Rummenigge spent 1974 to 1985 as a player with Bayern, serving as skipper from 1983 to 1984. He later became the club's president and then chairman. The German international won three Bundesliga Golden Boots and a European Golden Boot, along with two league titles and German Cups. He also helped Bayern hoist two European Cups and an Intercontinental Cup and was twice named European Footballer of the Year. Rummenigge, whose brother Michael also played for Bayern, notched 217 goals for the club in just over 400 games.

4. Attacker Rainer Ohlhauser spent 1961 to 1970 with Bayern, scoring 186 league goals in 286 games while tallying over 200 goals in all competitions. His scoring exploits helped the club earn promotion to the Bundesliga in 1965 as well as winning three German Cups, the UEFA Cup Winners' Cup in 1966-67, and the Bundesliga title in 1968-69. He left Munich and Germany in 1970, when he headed to Switzerland to play for Grasshopper in Zürich. Despite being one of Bayern's all-time top scorers, Ohlhauser played just once for the German national side.

5. Still climbing Bayern's all-time scoring ladder is Thomas Müller, who had 208 goals to his name in January 2021, while still playing for the club. The German international began his pro career with the team in 2008 and is quite versatile: he's been used as an attacking midfielder, winger,

second striker, and center forward. He's considered one of the club's best players ever for his teamwork, playmaking, work-rate, positioning, and stamina. Müller is one of the most decorated players in German football history, with several individual awards, and he has helped his team win nine league titles, six German Cups and German Super Cups, two European Champions Leagues, two UEFA Super Cups, and a FIFA Club World Cup.

6. Roland Wohlfarth was a West German forward who displayed an exceptional scoring touch for Bayern between 1984 and 1993, with 155 goals. He helped the squad win five league titles, a German Super Cup, and a German Cup. This included a hat trick in the 1985-86 German Cup in a 5-2 triumph over VfB Stuttgart. Wohlfarth shared the Bundesliga Golden Boot in 1988-89 and won it two seasons later with 21 goals. However, in 1995, while playing for VfL Bochum, he was banned for two months for taking anorectics.

7. Dieter Hoeneß, the younger brother of Bayern legend Uli Hoeneß, was a German international striker who joined the club from VfB Stuttgart in 1979. He scored 145 goals for the team before retiring in 1987. Along the way, Hoeneß won five league titles, along with three German Cups, and he made it to two European Cup finals. He was also a runner-up in the 1986 World Cup with West Germany and posted four goals in his six outings with the national senior side, also scoring two goals in two games with the B team.

8. Dutch international midfielder Arjen Robben joined Bayern in 2009 for a transfer fee of approximately €25 million and played 10 years for Die Roten. His partnership with Phillip Lahm and Frank Ribéry was one of the reasons for the club's success during his spell, while his speed and ball control made him one of the side's most valuable and entertaining players. He tallied 99 goals in 201 Bundesliga matches and 144 overall for Bayern while helping the team capture eight league titles, five German Cups and German Super Cups, the European Champions League, and a UEFA Super Cup. Robben was also named German Player of the Year and Bundesliga Player of the Year once each.

9. Brazilian international striker Giovane Élber, a wizard with the ball, was affectionately known as the "Samba Striker." He notched 140 goals in just over 260 games with Bayern between 1997 and 2003 and shared the Bundesliga Golden Boot in 2002-03. Élber helped the team win four league titles and League Cups, three German Cups, a European Champions League, the FIFA Club World Cup, and an Intercontinental Cup. He tallied 92 league goals in 169 matches thanks to his fantastic technique and pace. Élber left for Olympique Lyon in August 2003 and scored seven goals in 15 games for Brazil.

10. Striker Dieter Brenninger joined Bayern in 1962 and helped the side earn promotion to the Bundesliga in 1965 while playing in the Regionalliga Süd. Brenninger later won four German Cups with the team, as well as the

Bundesliga title and a European Cup Winners' Cup. He scored just over 130 goals with Bayern, with 59 of those coming in the Bundesliga. He left Munich in 1972 when he joined Young Boys Bern in Switzerland, before signing with VfB Stuttgart. Nicknamed "Mucki," Brenninger played just once for the German national side, in 1969.

# CONCLUSION

It's been over a century in the making, but what you have in front of you is a relatively comprehensive history of Bayern Munich in entertaining trivia form. With the club being so successful in its home nation and abroad, it's impossible to include everybody, but we trust all of your favorites are in here.

We hope you've enjoyed taking a look back at the team's stupendous history in such a lighthearted and entertaining manner and would be pleased if you've learned something new while doing so.

Armed with a dozen different chapters filled with quiz questions and an assortment of "Did You Know" facts, you should now be well prepared to challenge fellow Bavarians and other soccer fans to a wide range of quiz contests to determine who's left standing as the most knowledgeable.

We've included as many of the team's top players and managers as possible and provided a collection of informative and educational facts and trivia regarding the club's successes, transfers, records, and more.

We also hope you'll be inclined to share the trivia book with others to help teach Bayern Munich's marvelous history to those who may not be aware of it.

The ongoing history of Bayern Munich is fascinating, to say the least, and, at the rate the club's going, more records will soon be broken or solidified in the near future.

Thanks for being a loyal and passionate Bayern fan and taking the time to support the club and relive its memories by reading our trivia book.

Made in United States
Orlando, FL
20 December 2021